Year 6 Maths sorted — one week at a time!

This CGP book is packed with fantastic 10-Minute Workouts
for quick Maths practice sessions throughout Year 6.

There's one Workout for every week of the year, each covering
a mixture of topics and skills. They're perfect to use as
starter activities, recaps, homework tasks... and more!

We've even included a progress chart and answers to make
tracking how pupils are doing that much easier.

Published by CGP
ISBN: 978 1 78908 311 8

Editors: Sammy El-Bahrawy and Shaun Harrogate

Reviewer: Lucy Towle

With thanks to Liam Dyer and Maxine Petrie for
the proofreading.

Contents pages contain public sector information licensed
under the Open Government Licence v3.0.
http://www.nationalarchives.gov.uk/doc/open-
government-licence/version/3/

Clipart from Corel®

Printed by Elanders Ltd, Newcastle upon Tyne.
Based on the classic CGP style created by Richard Parsons.

Text, design, layout and original illustrations
© Coordination Group Publications Ltd. (CGP) 2019
All rights reserved.

How to Use this Book

- This book contains <u>36 workouts</u>. We've split them into <u>3 sections</u> — one for each term, with <u>12 workouts</u> each. There's roughly one workout for <u>every week</u> of the school year.

- Each workout is out of <u>12 marks</u> and should take about <u>10 minutes</u> to complete.

- Each workout starts with some <u>warm-up questions</u> covering the <u>number topics</u> and ends with a <u>problem solving question</u>.

- The <u>first 3 workouts</u> only contain <u>Year 5 Maths content</u> — they're ideal for <u>reminding</u> pupils what they learnt in the <u>previous year</u>. These workouts should be done at the <u>start</u> of Year 6.

- The <u>last 9 workouts</u> only contain <u>Year 6 content</u> — they're perfect for ensuring that pupils have <u>got to grips</u> with the Year 6 topics.

- The other workouts <u>increase in difficulty</u> as you go through the book. They contain a <u>mix</u> of topics from <u>Year 5</u> and <u>Year 6</u>.

- <u>Answers</u> and a <u>Progress Chart</u> can be found at the <u>back</u> of the book.

The <u>contents pages</u> show you where each Year 6 topic is <u>first introduced</u>.

In each term, the <u>new topics</u> are only tested in the workout they're listed under on the <u>contents page</u>. These topics are then retested in the <u>following terms</u>.

This means the workouts in each term can be done in <u>any order</u> — pick the workout which <u>best suits</u> the <u>needs</u> of your class.

The <u>tick boxes</u> on the contents pages can help you to keep a <u>record</u> of which workouts have been attempted.

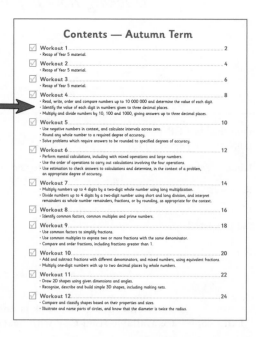

Contents — Autumn Term

Contents — Spring Term

Contents — Summer Term

Warm up

1. Work out the answers to these calculations.

   16.5 × 100 = ...   87 ÷ 100 = ...

   1.24 × 1000 = ...   5720 ÷ 1000 = ...

   <u>2 marks</u>

2. Work out the answers to these calculations.

   2 − 9 = ...   −3 + 5 = ...

   3 − 7 = ...   −2 + 8 = ...

   <u>2 marks</u>

3. Work out the size of **angle p** on the straight line below.

   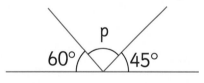

   angle p = ... °

   <u>1 mark</u>

4. 2 inches is approximately equal to 5 cm.
   How tall is the plant in **inches**?

   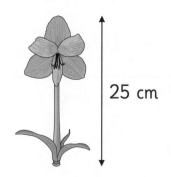

   25 cm

   .... inches

   <u>1 mark</u>

2

5. Look at the six number cards below.

7	2	9	3	2	1

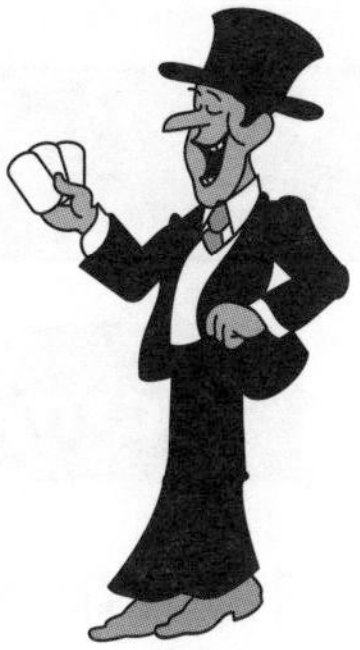

Rearrange the cards to make the **largest** possible number.

....

1 mark

Rearrange the cards to make the **smallest** possible number.

....

1 mark

6. A farmer collects **3253 eggs** from his chickens.
He can fit **6 eggs** in a box.
How many boxes will he need?

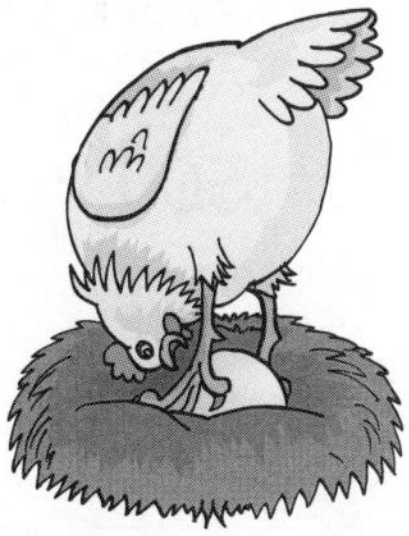

.... boxes

1 mark

7. Thor measured the temperatures inside two igloos every hour from 6 am till 10 am.
The line graph on the right shows his results.

How much more did the temperature in igloo A increase than the temperature in igloo B?

.... °C

3 marks

Score:

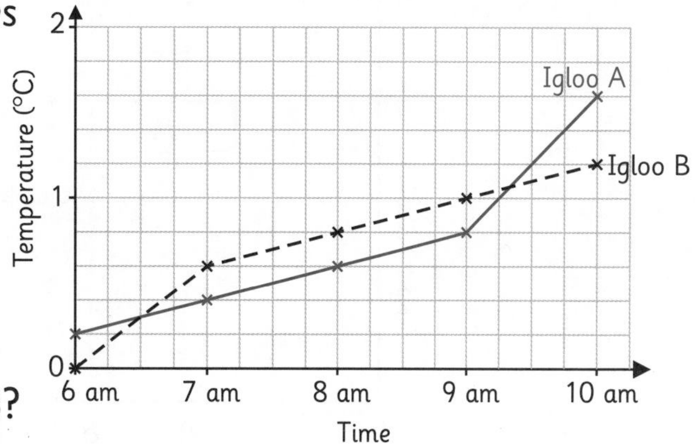

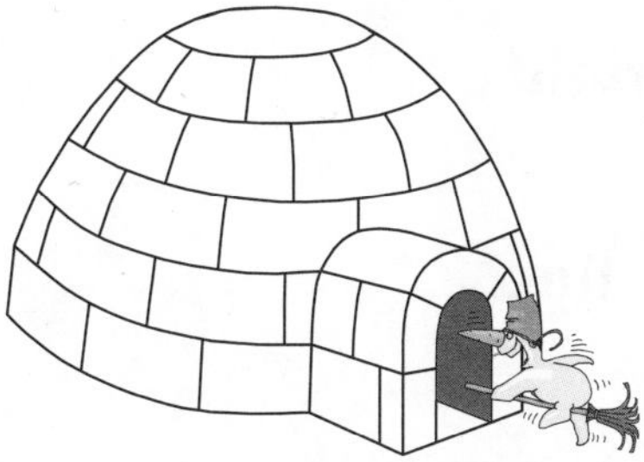

Warm up

1. Write down the value of each **underlined** digit.

    <u>5</u>17 802 ....   472 <u>0</u>00 ....

    7<u>6</u>4 245 ....   871 2<u>9</u>9 ....

    2 marks

2. Work out the answers to these calculations.

    500 × 5 = ...   7000 × 8 = ...

    2800 ÷ 4 = ...   5400 ÷ 9 = ...

    2 marks

3. Shape A has been drawn on the grid below.

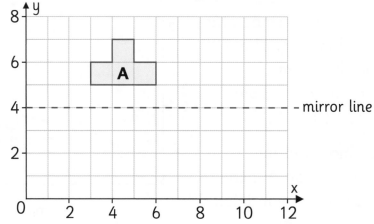 

Shape B is a translation of shape A **3 squares right** and **2 squares down**. Draw shape B.

1 mark

Shape C is a reflection of shape A in the **mirror line**. Draw shape C.

1 mark

4. Work out $\frac{3}{7} + \frac{6}{7}$.
    Give your answer as a **mixed number**.

    ....
    1 mark

5. What is the **perimeter** of the rectangle below?

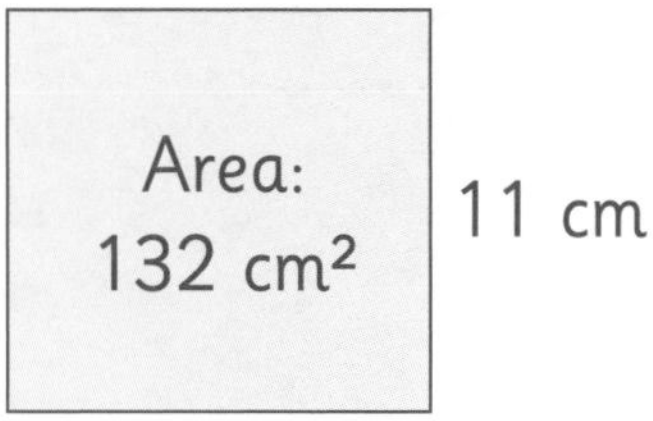

    Area:
    132 cm² | 11 cm

    .... cm
    2 marks

6. In a race, Vernon ran for **7 minutes 50 seconds**
    and walked for **2 minutes 30 seconds**.
    How long did it take him to complete the race?

    .... minutes .... seconds
    1 mark

7. Two arches and the years they were built are shown below.

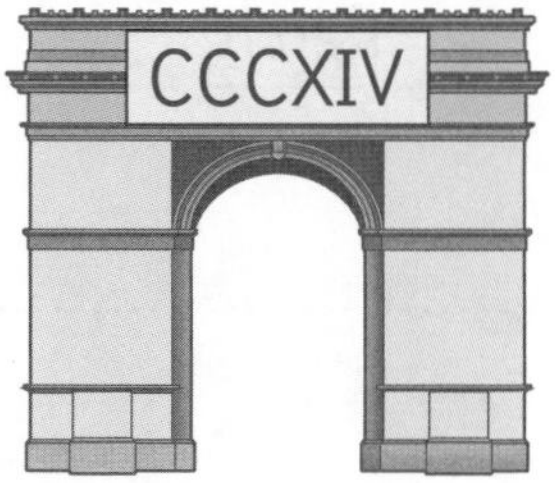

    CCCXIV   1809

    How many years apart were the two arches built?

    .... years
    2 marks

    Score:

Warm up

1. Round these decimals to the **nearest whole number**.

    2.5 ....   4.9 ....

    7.15 ....   8.22 ....

    2 marks

2. Fill in the missing numbers in these calculations.

    6400 + ... = 9400   .... − 2000 = 87 100

    5470 − .... = 4370   .... + 4400 = 19 670

    2 marks

3. There are four types of fish in a lake. The table on the right shows the percentage of each type of fish.

    What **percentage** of the fish are perch?

Name	Percentage
Barbel	17%
Pike	26%
Trout	30%
Perch	

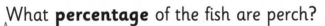

    .... %

    1 mark

4. Work out 452 × 23.

    ....

    1 mark

5. Helga has three identical beakers containing water.
   Beaker A is $\frac{2}{3}$ full, beaker B is $\frac{7}{12}$ full and beaker C is $\frac{5}{6}$ full.

   Put the beakers in order. Start with the
   beaker containing the **most water**.

   Beaker ....   Beaker ....   Beaker ....   _____
   2 marks

6. Write **true** or **false** next to the following statements.

   $62°$ is an acute angle.   ....

   Angles around a point add up to $180°$.   ....

   Obtuse angles are smaller than acute angles.   ....

   A right angle is exactly $90°$.   ....   _____
   2 marks

7. Caleb's toy bricks are each 9 mm tall.
   He stacks them up to make a 1.26 m tower.
   How many bricks did Caleb use?

   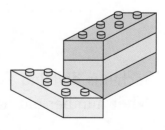

   .... bricks   _____
   2 marks

   Score: [   ]

Warm up

1. Count up in **steps of 0.4** to complete this sequence.

    12.9   13.3   ....

    1 mark

2. Work out the answers to these calculations.

    1200 + 7000 = ...   58 300 – 5000 = ...

    7420 – 1400 = ...   16 500 + 9300 = ...

    2 marks

3. Emma works out that it is **2 332 850 seconds** until her birthday. Write this number in **words**.

    ....

    ....

    1 mark

4. Sachin is dividing 7634 by **10, 100 and 1000**. What number did he divide by if he gets:

    a 3 in the tenths place?   ....

    1 mark

    a 4 in the thousandths place?   ....

    1 mark

5. Each cube in the 3D shape below has a volume of **1 cm³**.

What is the total **volume** of the shape?

.... cm³

6. Write the value of the **underlined** digit in these numbers.

9.<u>8</u>31   ....   15.78<u>2</u>   ....

7. Every hour, you blink approximately **1000 times** and each blink lasts for about **0.352 seconds**. How many seconds do you spend blinking each hour?

.... seconds

8. 2000 aliens live on a distant planet. $\frac{1}{5}$ of the aliens have one eye, $\frac{3}{4}$ of the aliens have two eyes and the rest have three eyes.

How many eyes do the aliens have in total?

.... eyes

Score:

Warm up

1. Write down all the **factors of 50**.

    ....

    1 mark

2. Write these amounts as **percentages**.

    0.34 = ... % $\frac{29}{100}$ = ... %

    0.8 = ... % $\frac{2}{5}$ = ... %

    2 marks

3. The table below shows temperatures recorded on one day in different countries.

Location	Canada	Australia	Russia	Uruguay
Temperature	–7 °C	31 °C	–15 °C	17°C

    What is the **difference** in temperature between:

    the two coldest countries?

    .... °C

    1 mark

    the hottest country and
    the coldest country?

    .... °C

    1 mark

4. Round these numbers to the **nearest 1 000 000**.

    1 532 100   ....   8 754 215   ....

5. Circle the correct net of a **cube**.

6. A lottery winner bought three cars for £42 000, £20 000
    and £96 500. How much did they spend in **total**?
    Give your answer to the **nearest £10 000**.

    £ ....

7. Eight friends went out trick-or-treating on Halloween.
    Five of the friends got 233 sweets each.
    Three of the friends got 387 sweets each.
    They decide to share the sweets
    equally between them.

    How many sweets are left?

    .... sweets

    Score:

(10)

Warm up

1. Fill in the gaps in these number sentences using **<** or **>**.

    12 087 .... 12 078   475 400 .... 457 400

    152 100 .... 152 500   945 500 .... 954 200

    2 marks

2. Work out the answers to these calculations.

    $\frac{1}{8} \times 5 =$ .... $\frac{3}{11} \times 3 =$ ....

    1 mark

3. **Tick** the **two** correct calculations below.

    $6 + 4 \times 6 = 60$ ☐ $9 \div 3 + 6 = 9$ ☐

    $12 - 4 \div 2 = 4$ ☐ $11 + 2 \times 2 = 15$ ☐

    2 marks

4. Use a protractor and ruler to draw a **130° angle** below.

    _____

    1 mark

5. Work out these calculations **in your head**.

    320 000 – 50 000 × 4

    .... _____
    1 mark

    (432 000 + 123 000) – 40 000

    .... _____
    1 mark

6. Larry drives his truck 2848 km each week. He calculates
    that he drives 2848 × 52 = 148 096 km in one year.

    Write an estimation calculation he could do **in his
    head** to **check** whether his answer is **correct**.

    .... _____
    1 mark

    Work out the answer to your calculation.

    .... km _____
    1 mark

7. The poster shows the start and end times
    of three events at the local sports centre.

    How many minutes longer does the
    badminton event last than the hopathon?

    Badminton
    08:25 - 11:15
    Jousting
    11:15 - 11:55
    Hopathon
    11:55 - 13:10

    .... minutes _____
    2 marks

    Score: [   ]

Warm up

1. Put these decimals in order. Start with the **largest**.

    3.45   3.4   3.402   3.5   3.54

    ....

    largest   smallest

    2 marks

2. Circle all the fractions which are **equivalent to $\frac{2}{3}$**.

    $\frac{4}{6}$ $\frac{8}{9}$ $\frac{9}{12}$ $\frac{10}{15}$ $\frac{20}{30}$ $\frac{30}{45}$ $\frac{50}{60}$

    2 marks

3. Ida has **4275 plants** and she can fit **12 plants** in each pot. How many pots will she need?

    .... pots

    1 mark

4. What **percentages** of these grids are shaded?

    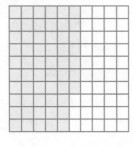   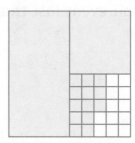

    .... %   .... %

    2 marks

5. Circle all the shapes below that have a **circular face**.

   cone   cuboid   square-based pyramid   cylinder   cube

   _____
   1 mark

6. There are **54 pages** in a magazine about kangaroos.

   How many pages are there in **2647** of these magazines?

   .... pages

   _____
   1 mark

   The 2647 magazines were shared equally between **22 shops**.
   How many were left over?

   .... magazines

   _____
   1 mark

7. Calculate the perimeter of the shape below.
   Give your answer in millimetres.

   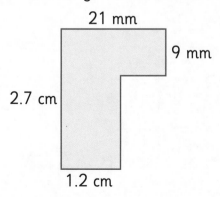

   21 mm
   9 mm
   2.7 cm
   1.2 cm

   .... mm

   _____
   2 marks

   Score: [   ]

(10)

Warm up

1. Write the following numbers in **digits**.

    Fifty seven thousand and forty nine   ....

    Six hundred thousand two hundred and two ....

    1 mark

2. Circle the decimals that **round to 8.4** to 1 decimal place.

    8.51   8.47   8.44   8.45   8.35

    1 mark

3. Circle all of the numbers below which are
    common multiples of 5 and 7.

    28   50   70   100   140

        150   350   500   750

    1 mark

4. Each square on the grids below is **1 m²**.
    Estimate the **area** of each shape.

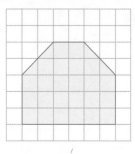   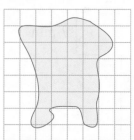

    .... m²   .... m²

    2 marks

16

5. Find all the **common factors** of 18 and 42.

.... 1 mark

6. **45%** of Andy's ties are stripy, $\frac{19}{50}$ are spotty and the rest are plain. What **percentage** of his ties are plain?

.... %
2 marks

7. How many **common multiples** of 3 and 11 are also **prime numbers**? Explain your answer.

....

.... 2 marks

8. Every hour, the minute hand on a clock face turns 360°. How many degrees in total does the minute hand turn between 07:55 and 10:10?

.... °
2 marks

Score:

Autumn Term: Workout 9

1. Write down the **value of the 8** in each of these numbers.

   87.10 ....   5.68 ....

   0.85 ....   18.77 ....

   2 marks

2. Count **down** in steps of **10 000** from 122 400.

   122 400   ....

   1 mark

3. **Simplify** the following fractions.

   $\frac{20}{25}$ = ... $\frac{28}{70}$ = ...

   1 mark

4. Circle the **best estimate** for the size of **angle x** below.

   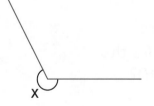

   160°   240°

   270°   300°

   1 mark

5. Circle the **largest** improper fraction.

   $\frac{23}{10}$ $\frac{11}{5}$ $\frac{34}{15}$ $\frac{67}{30}$

   1 mark

6. A cricket ball has a mass of **160 g**.
    What is the mass of **20 cricket balls** in kg?

    .... kg $\overline{\text{2 marks}}$

7. Look at the fractions below.

    $\dfrac{2}{3}$ $\dfrac{11}{12}$ $\dfrac{7}{8}$ $\dfrac{7}{9}$

    Which two fractions are **smaller than** $\dfrac{5}{6}$?

    .... and .... $\overline{\text{2 marks}}$

8. The table on the right shows the prices
    of some jewels. If you buy two jewels
    then you get them half price.

    Leon bought two jewels and paid £23 340.

    Which jewels did he buy?

    | Ruby | £25 510 |
    | Sapphire | £14 530 |
    | Emerald | £22 170 |
    | Diamond | £32 150 |

    .... and .... $\overline{\text{2 marks}}$

    Score:

Autumn Term: Workout 9

Autumn Term: Workout 10

Warm up

1. Put these numbers in order. Start with the **smallest**.

    155 233   155 323   153 533   153 333

    ....   _____
    smallest   largest   1 mark

2. Cross out the **six numbers** below which are **not prime**.

    2   5   8   9   11   15   19

    23   25   28   31   33   37

    _____
    2 marks

3. Work out $7^2 + 2^3$.

    ....   _____
    1 mark

4. A lap around a local park is **1.41 miles**.
    How many miles is:

    2 laps?

    .... miles   _____
    1 mark

    7 laps?

    .... miles   _____
    1 mark

20

5. **Reflect** the shape on the grid below in the mirror line.

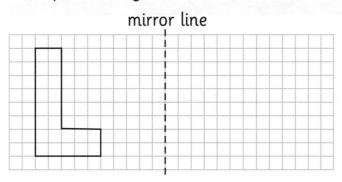

mirror line

6. Luigi has $\frac{5}{8}$ **kg** of potatoes and $1\frac{1}{3}$ **kg** of sweet potatoes.
    How many kg of ingredients does he have in **total**?

    .... kg

    How much **more** do the sweet potatoes
    weigh than the regular potatoes?

    .... kg

7. Hannah drinks 110 ml of milk each day from Monday to
    Friday and 150 ml each day on Saturday and Sunday.
    How many litres of milk will she drink in 6 weeks?

    .... litres

Score:

Warm up

1. Fill in the gaps with either **10**, **100** or **1000**.

    0.93 × .... = 93   45.1 ÷ .... = 4.51

    7.84 × .... = 7840   547 ÷ .... = 5.47

    2 marks

2. Circle all of the **square numbers** below.

    4   10   27   36   50   64   88

    1 mark

3. Complete the net of the **cuboid** on the grid below.

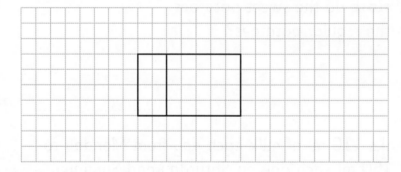 

1 mark

4. Complete the factor trees to find the
    prime factors of these numbers.

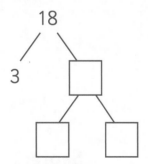 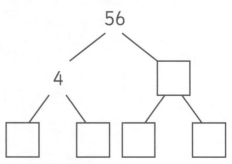

2 marks

5. Use a ruler and protractor to accurately draw this triangle.

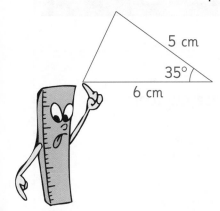

5 cm

35°

6 cm

Measure the length of the unlabelled side to the **nearest mm**.

.... mm

6. Complete these sentences.

87 542 rounded to the nearest .... is 87 500.

587 542 rounded to the nearest .... is 590 000.

7. Jenny has $2\frac{5}{6}$ kg of flour. She uses $\frac{2}{3}$ kg to make some bread and takes the rest to her grandma.
Her grandma says, "Thanks Jenny, but I don't need any more flour. I already have three times as much as you."

How much flour does her grandma have?

Flour

.... kg

Score:

Warm up

1. Write the **Roman numerals** that represent these numbers.

    9 ....   23 ....

    54 ....   112 ....

2. Change these mixed numbers into **improper fractions**.

    $1\frac{1}{4}$ = ... $4\frac{1}{2}$ = ...

    $2\frac{3}{4}$ = ... $3\frac{2}{3}$ = ...

3. Write these words in the correct place on the diagram.

    circumference   radius   diameter

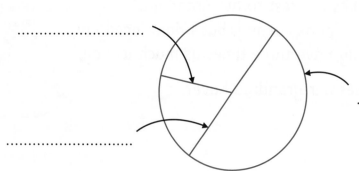

    ....

    ....

    ....

4. If the radius of a circle is **10 cm**, what is its diameter?

    .... cm

5. Write the **full names** of the shapes being described below.

A 3D shape with 2 triangular faces and 3 rectangular faces.

....

A 2D shape with three angles of sizes 58°, 64° and 58°.

....

6. Nigel's house is worth **£428 440**.
Kim's house is worth **half as much** as Nigel's.
Lydia's house is worth **£25 200** more than Kim's.

How much is Lydia's house worth?

£ ....

7. Omar starts off with 4.5 litres of orange juice.
He fills nine 0.3 litre glasses and four 220 ml glasses.

How many litres of orange juice does he have left?

.... litres

Score:

Warm up

1. Round these numbers to the **nearest 1000**.

   42 300 ....

   678 510 ....

   899 654 ....

   4 972 542 ....

   _____
   2 marks

2. Circle two fractions that are **equivalent to** $\dfrac{22}{33}$.

   $\dfrac{2}{3}$ $\qquad$ $\dfrac{3}{2}$ $\qquad$ $\dfrac{11}{12}$ $\qquad$ $\dfrac{4}{6}$ $\qquad$ $\dfrac{22}{30}$

   _____
   1 mark

3. A researcher is tracking the heights above sea level of a bird and a fish. The bird is at **43 m** and the fish is at **−21 m**. What is the **difference** in their heights?

   .... m
   _____
   1 mark

4. Work out these multiplications. Simplify your answers.

   $\dfrac{3}{4} \times \dfrac{2}{5}$

   ....
   _____
   1 mark

   $\dfrac{5}{6} \times \dfrac{4}{10}$

   ....
   _____
   1 mark

5. What is another name for
    the **perimeter of a circle**? ....
    1 mark

6. A biscuit factory makes **8632 gingerbread men** every hour.
    How many can the factory make in **16 hours?**

    ....
    1 mark

7. Circle the calculations below that are **correct**.

    $\dfrac{2}{3} \div 3 = \dfrac{2}{6}$ $\dfrac{5}{9} \div 4 = \dfrac{20}{9}$ $\dfrac{3}{10} \div 2 = \dfrac{3}{20}$

    $\dfrac{9}{11} \div 3 = \dfrac{3}{11}$ $\dfrac{7}{8} \div 5 = \dfrac{8}{35}$ $\dfrac{8}{9} \div 8 = \dfrac{1}{9}$

    2 marks

8. The line graph shows
    how the prices of two
    chocolate bars changed
    from 2015 to 2019.

    What was the biggest price
    difference between the bars
    from 2015 to 2019?

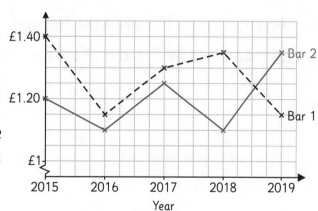

    .... p
    2 marks

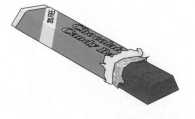

    Score: [   ]

Warm up

1. Circle all the **multiples of 25**.

    1   5   25   70   75   135

    300   450   540   615   855   1025

    2 marks

2. Work out the answers to these calculations **in your head**.

    5400 + 1200 = ...   34 400 – 3100 = ...

    9870 – 2220 = ...   43 960 + 5030 = ...

    2 marks

3. Angelica says, "To write the fraction $\frac{14}{64}$ as a decimal I can **divide 7 by 32**." Do you agree? Explain your answer.

    ....

    ....

    1 mark

4. Work out **574.3 ÷ 2**.

    ....

    1 mark

5. Complete the **net** of this shape on the grid below.

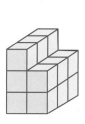

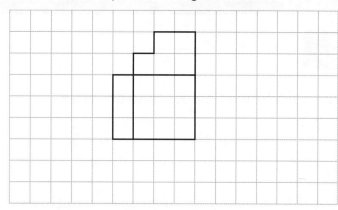

2 marks

6. Use **division** to write the following fractions as **decimals**.

$\frac{3}{8}$

.... 1 mark

$\frac{7}{20}$

.... 1 mark

7. Trey's aeroplane teaspoon can hold 5.12 ml of liquid.
He has a 50 ml bottle of vanilla extract and uses 7 teaspoons.
How much is left in the bottle?

.... ml 2 marks

Score:

10

Warm up

1. Circle the calculations below that are **true**.

    $3^3 = 27$ $5^2 = 10$ $2^3 = 6$ $7^2 = 49$

    _____
    1 mark

2. Work out the following as **improper fractions**.

    $\frac{3}{7} \times 4 =$ .... $\frac{8}{9} \times 7 =$ ....

    $\frac{4}{5} \times 12 =$ .... $\frac{5}{6} \times 5 =$ ....

    _____
    2 marks

3. A chocolate bar is 53% sugar.
    What **fraction** of the chocolate bar is **not sugar**?

    ....
    _____
    1 mark

4. Translate this shape **4 squares up** and **6 squares left**.

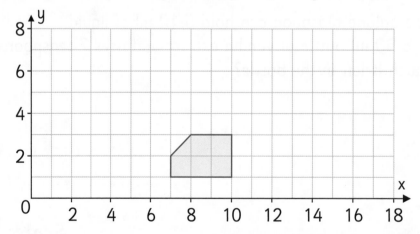

    _____
    1 mark

5. Fill in the gaps in this number machine.

$$\boxed{8.74} \xrightarrow{\times 100} \text{......................} \xrightarrow{\div 1000} \text{......................}$$

1 mark

6. Sid has finished $\frac{7}{20}$ of the levels in a computer game, Zainab has finished **34%** and Meg has finished $\frac{1}{3}$. Who has finished **more** levels? Show your working.

....

2 marks

7. Bottle A can hold **700 ml** and is **15%** full.
Bottle B can hold **300 ml** and is **40%** full.
Which bottle has **more** liquid? Show your working.

Bottle ....

2 marks

8. Every hour, 6 875 000 cups of tea and 2 815 000 cups of coffee are drunk in the UK. How many more cups of tea than cups of coffee are drunk in 3 hours?

.... cups

2 marks

Score: [ ]

Warm up

1. Circle the numbers with an **8** in the **tenths** place.

   87.42   74.83   64.18   1.847   8.99   82.1

   _____
   1 mark

2. Work out the answers to these calculations **in your head**.

   5000 × 30 = ...   32 000 ÷ 80 = ...

   900 × 700 = ...   60 000 ÷ 200 = ...

   _____
   2 marks

3. Circle all of the **common factors** of 12 and 40.

1	2	3	4	6
10	12	20	24	40

   _____
   1 mark

4. Idris and Lev share **270 peanuts**.
   For every peanut that Idris gets, Lev gets two.
   How many peanuts does Lev get?

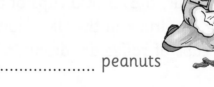

   .... peanuts

   _____
   1 mark

5. Theo's house is worth **£2 150 000** to the **nearest £10 000**.
   Circle the **lowest** possible value of his house.

   £2 100 000   £2 140 000   £2 145 000

   _____
   1 mark

6. Put these shapes in the correct place in the table below.

Rhombus   Equilateral Triangle   Rectangle   Regular Pentagon

	No obtuse angles	Obtuse angles
2 lines of symmetry		
More than 2 lines of symmetry		

2 marks

7. **30 pupils** are split into two groups in the ratio **2:3**.

How many pupils are in the smaller group?

.... pupils

1 mark

How many pupils are in the larger group?

.... pupils

1 mark

8. The shape below is made from 4 identical rectangles.
What is the area of the shaded part of the shape?

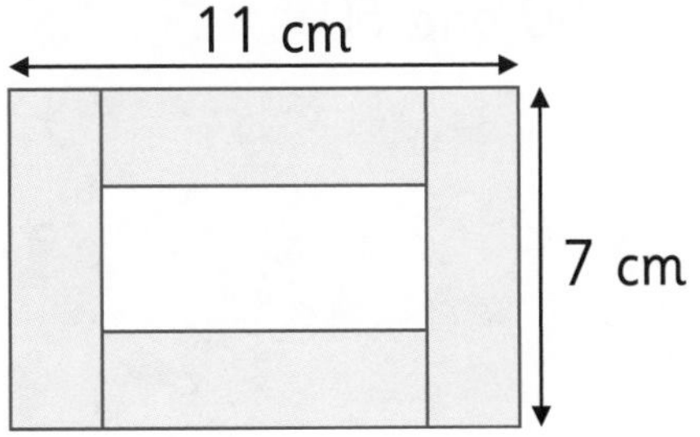

11 cm

7 cm

.... cm^2

2 marks

Score:

33

10

---

1. Fill in the gaps in these number sentences using **<, = or >**.

   $\dfrac{5}{8}$ .... $\dfrac{1}{2}$ $\dfrac{1}{3}$ .... $\dfrac{4}{9}$

   $\dfrac{3}{4}$ .... $\dfrac{9}{12}$ $\dfrac{3}{5}$ .... $\dfrac{7}{10}$

   2 marks

2. Count **up** in steps of **1000** from 747 300.

   747 300 ....

   1 mark

---

3. The square below is enlarged by a **scale factor of 5**.
   What will the **side length** of the enlarged shape be?

   7 cm

   .... cm

   1 mark

4. Find all of the **prime numbers** between 50 and 60.

   ....

   2 marks

---

5. At chess club, for every **3 humans** there are **8 robots**.

If there are 9 humans, how many robots are there?

.... robots

If there are 72 robots, how many humans are there?

.... humans

6. Look at the shapes on the right. What is the **scale factor** of enlargement from the smaller shape to the bigger shape?

80 cm

5.6 m

....

7. An indoor arena has 18 seated sections each containing the same number of seats. Jaspreet counts 5434 seats in total. Has he counted correctly? Explain your answer.

....

....

Score:

Spring Term: Workout 6

Warm up

1. Round these decimals to **one decimal place**.

   0.15 ....   7.04 ....

   16.91 ....   42.97 ....

   2 marks

2. Work out the following. Give answers as **mixed numbers**.

   $3\frac{6}{7} - \frac{4}{7} =$ .... $2\frac{1}{5} - \frac{2}{5} =$ ....

   1 mark

3. Write down the **rule** and the **next term** for each of these sequences.

   −12   −5   2   9   16

   ....

   1 mark

   700   550   400   250

   ....

   1 mark

4. Circle the **reflex angle**.

   1 mark

5. Felicity uses this formula to work out
    how many minutes a chicken takes to cook:

    Total time (minutes) = 40 × Weight (kg) + 10

    How long will a **2.5 kg** chicken take to cook?

.... minutes

6. Shin is travelling from
    East Port to **Snail Cove**.

    Which ferry takes the **least** time
    to get between these places?
    Show your working.

	Ferry A	Ferry B	Ferry C
East Port	11:30	12:55	14:20
Crab Point	12:57	14:25	15:43
Snail Cove	13:17	14:39	16:05
West Port	13:33	14:58	16:23

Ferry ....

7. The **formula** for the term in position **n** of a sequence
    is **4n + 1**. Write down the **first 3 terms** in the sequence.

    ....

8. Tamal and Una both start with the number 1 857 647.
    Tamal rounds it to the nearest 100 000
    and Una rounds it to the nearest 10 000.
    What is the difference between their answers?

....

Score:

37

10

1. Count up in **steps of $\frac{2}{5}$**.

    $\frac{4}{5}$ $1\frac{1}{5}$ ....

2. Fill in the missing numbers in these calculations.

    $-2 -$ .... $= -8$ .... $+ 7 = 3$

    .... $- 5 = -1$ $-4 +$ .... $= 2$

3. Arthur digs a circular hole
    with a diameter of **25 cm**.
    What is the radius of the hole?

    .... cm

4. Steph is thinking of a number, **x**.
    She **multiplies it by 4** and **subtracts 7** to get **17**.

    Write an **equation** involving x.

    ....

    What is the value of x?

    x = ...

5. Circle the values for which **both** of the equations on the right are **true**.

$A - B = 2$
$3A + B = 14$

A = 3, B = 1   A = 4, B = 2   A = 2, B = 8

1 mark

6. Rearrange the digits in 5 787 243 to make the **largest odd number** that you can.

....

1 mark

7. The shapes in this equation stand for **whole numbers bigger than 0**.

$5 \times$ ☆ $+$ ◯ $= 19$

List **all** the possible pairs of values of the shapes.

☆ = ...   ◯ = ...

☆ = ...   ◯ = ...

☆ = ...   ◯ = ...

2 marks

8. One day a zoo had 6000 visitors. $\frac{4}{5}$ of the visitors were adults and $\frac{1}{4}$ of the adults went to the butterfly house.

How many adults visited the butterfly house?

.... adults

2 marks

Score:

Spring Term: Workout 7

⏱ 10

Warm up

1. Convert these decimals to **fractions** and **simplify**.

   0.3 = ...   0.29 = ...

   0.62 = ...   0.15 = ...

   2 marks

2. Work out the value of these **Roman numerals**.

   CLXV ....   XLVI ....

   1 mark

3. Gemma's fingernails are **1.789 cm** long and Jessie's are **20.24 mm** long. How many mm longer are Jessie's fingernails than Gemma's?

   .... mm

   2 marks

4. Work out **3.78 × 9**.

   ....

   1 mark

5. Draw a parallelogram with sides of **3 cm** and **5 cm** and angles of **45°** and **135°**.

2 marks

6. Two pirates, Pete and Hacksaw, are hunting for some treasure. Pete is **64 km** from the treasure and Hacksaw is **45 miles** from the treasure. Approximately how many **miles** closer is Pete than Hacksaw?

.... miles

2 marks

7. The bar chart below shows the number of 400 m, 800 m and 1500 m races Lee ran in a year.

How many km did he run in total?

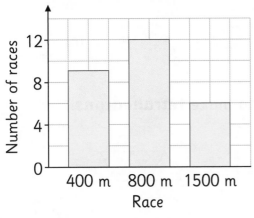

.... km

2 marks

Score:

Spring Term: Workout 8

Warm up

1. Fill in the missing numbers in these calculations.

   20 × .... = 40 000   9000 ÷ .... = 300

   .... × 300 = 36 000   .... ÷ 200 = 160

   _____
   2 marks

2. Convert these decimals to **percentages**.

   0.34 = ... %   0.9 = ... %

   _____
   1 mark

3. The table shows how much water three rabbits drink in a day.

   How many ml of water did they drink in **total**?

Jumpy	0.423 litres
Speedy	199 ml
Snoozy	0.24 litres

   .... ml

   _____
   2 marks

4. Circle the two nets which will fold up to make **tetrahedrons**.

   _____
   1 mark

5. It takes Ryan **6 minutes 42 seconds** to do the washing up. His mum can do it in **half** the time. How many **seconds** does it take his mum?

.... seconds

6. Circle the numbers which are **equivalent to** $\frac{10}{6}$.

$$\frac{5}{3} \qquad 1\frac{2}{6} \qquad \frac{22}{12} \qquad \frac{15}{9}$$

7. Rachel has a **6 kg baggage** allowance on a flight. Her clothes weigh **3.875 kg** and the bag weighs **900 g**.

How many grams of her baggage allowance are left?

.... g

8. A mining robot can collect 451 rocks every hour. The robot runs constantly for 8 hours. The rocks are then divided equally into 18 crates.

How many rocks are left over? Show your working.

.... rocks

Score:

Warm up

1. Fill in the missing numbers in these calculations.

    .... + 2100 = 9000   34 400 – .... = 28 400

    .... – 5040 = 3520   71 080 + ... = 80 280

    <u>2 marks</u>

2. Fill in the **missing fractions** to complete these calculations.

    $0.347 = \dfrac{3}{10} + \dfrac{4}{100} + \ ....$ $0.039 = \ .... + \dfrac{9}{1000}$

    <u>1 mark</u>

3. Write the following number in **digits**.

    Six million, four hundred and
    two thousand, five hundred and ten.   ....

    <u>1 mark</u>

4. Find the **missing angles** in these shapes:

    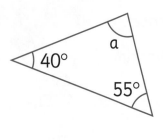

    $a =$ ....° $b =$ ....°

    <u>2 marks</u>

---

5. Use **+**, **−**, **×** or **÷** to fill in the gaps in the calculation below.

$$65 \;\underline{\dots\dots} \; 5 \; \underline{\dots\dots} \; 5 = 40$$

6. An **isosceles triangle** is shown below.
    Find the values of **x** and **y**.

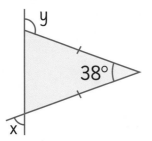

x = ...°

y = ...°

7. The exterior angles of a polygon add up to 360°.
    What is the **name** of the regular polygon
    that has **exterior angles** of **60°**?

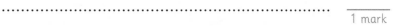

8. Siobhan is thinking of a two-digit number. She says, "my
    number is one more than a square number and has 6 factors."

    What number is Siobhan thinking of?

....

Score:

Warm up

1. Count down in **steps of 7**.

    17   10   ....

    1 mark

2. Convert these fractions to **decimals**.

    $\frac{7}{10}$ = ... $\frac{97}{100}$ = ...

    $\frac{3}{5}$ = ... $\frac{21}{50}$ = ...

    2 marks

3. Find the **area** of these shapes.

    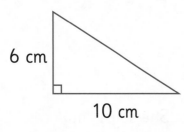

    6 cm

    10 cm

    8 m

    7 m

    .... cm²   .... m²

    2 marks

4. Greta claims that, **"91 is a prime number."**
    Do you agree? Explain your answer.

    ....

    ....

    1 mark

5. A sack of rice has a mass of **5.43 kg** and a wooden pallet has a mass of **15 kg**. What is the **total mass** of a pallet containing **1000 sacks** of rice?

.... kg

6. The table shows the length, width and area of three rectangles. All the rectangles have a **perimeter of 40 cm**. Complete the table.

Rectangle	Length	Width	Area
A	2 cm		
B		10 cm	
C			19 cm²

7. Margaret and Betty are knitting a 4 m long scarf. So far, Margaret has knitted $1\frac{1}{8}$ m and Betty has knitted $\frac{2}{3}$ m. How many more metres do they need to knit? Give your answer as a mixed number.

.... m

Score:

10

1. Work out the answers to these calculations.

    5.05 – 2.02 = ...   5.47 + 1.32 = ...

    4.3 + 1.59 = ...   8.5 – 3.48 = ...

    2 marks

2. Work out the following. Give your answers as **decimals**.

    $\dfrac{7}{10} + \dfrac{1}{100} + \dfrac{8}{1000} =$ .... $\dfrac{3}{10} + \dfrac{47}{1000} =$ ....

    1 mark

3. A toy cube has a side length of 5 cm.
    What is the **volume** of the toy cube?

    .... cm^3

    1 mark

4. Put these fractions in order. Start with the **largest**.

    $\dfrac{5}{4}$ $\dfrac{11}{8}$ $\dfrac{4}{3}$ $\dfrac{17}{12}$

    ....

    largest   smallest

    2 marks

5. Work out the **volumes** of the cuboids below.

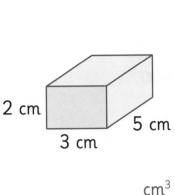

2 cm
5 cm
3 cm

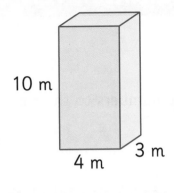

10 m
4 m
3 m

.... cm³

.... m³

6. Write down all the **common multiples** of 9 and 15 that are less than 100.

....

7. A pet shop sells boxes of 19 crickets.
Samir estimates the number of crickets in 2404 boxes by rounding each number to the nearest 10.
How far will his estimate be from the actual value?

.........................crickets

Score:

Summer Term: Workout 1

Warm up

1. Round these numbers to the **nearest 100 000**.

    3 157 400 ....   1 995 100 ....

    _____
    1 mark

2. Work out these fraction calculations.

    $\frac{1}{9} \times \frac{1}{2} =$ .... $\frac{1}{5} \times \frac{3}{4} =$ ....

    $\frac{3}{8} \times \frac{3}{5} =$ .... $\frac{7}{9} \times \frac{7}{10} =$ ....

    _____
    2 marks

3. Circle the name of the 3D shape that has **5 faces**, **5 vertices** and **8 edges**.

    Tetrahedron   Triangular prism

    Square-based pyramid   Cube

    _____
    1 mark

4. A librarian equally splits **5103 books** across **21 bookcases**. How many books are in each bookcase?

    .... books

    _____
    1 mark

5. A cuboid is **10 cm** long. Its width is **half** its length and its height is **six times** its width. What is its **volume**?

    .... cm^3

    _____
    2 marks

6. Look at shape A on the grid below.

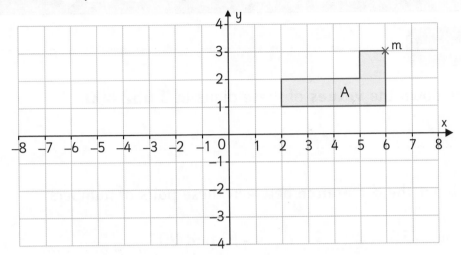

Reflect shape A in the **x-axis**. Label this shape **B**.

1 mark

Translate shape A **–7 units horizontally**
and **+1 unit vertically**. Label this shape **C**.

1 mark

Write down the coordinates of **point m** on **shape B**.

(........... , ...)

1 mark

7. In a sale, some jeans which were £40 now have £6 off.
    A shirt which was £25 is now £21.
    Which item has the biggest percentage discount?
    Show your working.

....

2 marks

Score:

10

Warm up

1. Write down the **values** of these digits in **3 652 400**.

    3 ....   5 ....

    1 mark

2. Work out the **difference** between these pairs of numbers.

    −18 and −30 ....   −12 and 20 ....

    49 and −10 ....   −20 and 37 ....

    2 marks

3. Winston measured the depth of water in a birdbath
    every morning at 00:01 for 7 days. Here are his results.

Day	Mon	Tues	Wed	Thurs	Fri	Sat	Sun
Depth (cm)	1.2	0.7	0.2	0.9	1.1	0.5	0.1

Draw a **line graph** of Winston's data on this grid.

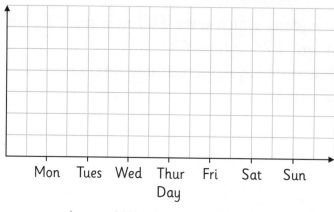

2 marks

It rained on **two** days. Which two days do you think it was?

.... and ....

1 mark

4. Write down a **calculation** you could do to **estimate** the answer to (302 186 + 593 213) × 9.87.

....
1 mark

5. Work out the **mean** of the numbers in the box on the right.

| 12 | 15 | 9 | 11 | 13 |

....
1 mark

6. The diagram shows a sketch of a field in the shape of a **parallelogram**. What is the **area** of the field?

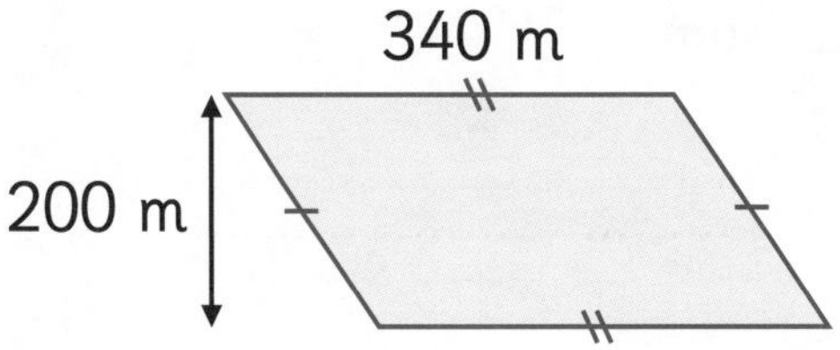

340 m

200 m

.... m²
1 mark

7. A jar contains 18 scoops of chocolate powder. 4 scoops of powder can make 300 ml of milkshake. How many litres of milkshake can 3 jars of chocolate powder make?

.... litres
3 marks

Score:

Warm up

1. Circle the formula that generates the sequence: **4, 7, 10, 13**

   3n   4n   3n + 1   5n − 1

   _____
   1 mark

2. Fill in the missing numbers in these calculations.

   120 000 × .... = 720 000   3000 × .... = 150 000

   64 000 ÷ .... = 8000   810 000 ÷ .... = 9000

   _____
   2 marks

3. What name is given to the distance from the **edge of a circle** to the **centre**?

   ....

   _____
   1 mark

4. Some bunting is $\frac{5}{6}$ **m long**. How long would each piece be if it was chopped into 10 pieces?

   .... m

   _____
   1 mark

5. On a school trip, **32%** of the pupils had juice, $\frac{7}{25}$ had water and the rest had both.

   What percentage of pupils had both?

   .... %

   _____
   2 marks

6. The table on the right shows the favourite fruits of **30 girls**.

Fruit	Apple	Orange	Banana
Number	15	5	10
Angle	180°	60°	120°

Complete the pie chart below to show this information.

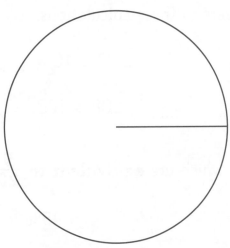

If **4 girls** change their answer from Apple to Kiwi, how big will the **angle** for Kiwi be on the pie chart?

°

....

7. Yusuf has a 2 m space next to his bed. He wants to put two sets of 0.784 m wide drawers and a 41.7 cm wide mirror in the space. Will they all fit? Show your working.

....

Score:

Summer Term: Workout 4

Warm up

1. Work out the answers to these calculations.

    1.578 × 100 = ...   3.87 ÷ 10 = ...

    7.004 × 1000 = ...   2508 ÷ 1000 = ...

    <u>2 marks</u>

2. Circle the amounts which are **equivalent to** $\frac{9}{20}$.

    0.45   90%   0.9   45% $\frac{18}{100}$

    <u>1 mark</u>

3. Look at the rectangle on the right.

    What are the coordinates
    of **point p**?

    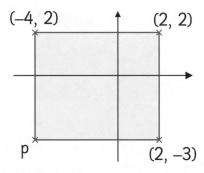

    (........... , ...)

    <u>1 mark</u>

4. Marta has $\frac{3}{8}$ of her birthday cake left. She gives
    $\frac{1}{4}$ of what is left to her teacher. What **fraction** of
    the **whole birthday cake** did she give to her teacher?

    ....

    <u>1 mark</u>

56

5. Circle all the numbers that are **prime** and **common factors** of 56 and 84.

   1   2   3   4   6   7   14   21   28

6. Simon is allowed to go to band practice for **5 hours** each week. He played for **1 hour 7 minutes** on Monday, **93 minutes** on Tuesday and **29 minutes** on Wednesday.

   How many minutes does he have left this week?

   .... minutes

7. Find the missing **fraction** in this calculation.

$$............ + 1\frac{3}{4} = 2\frac{7}{12}$$

8. The perimeter of the rectangle on the right is 20 cm. What is the area of the rectangle after an enlargement by scale factor 5?

   3 cm

   .... cm^2

   Score:

(10)

Warm up

1. Fill in the missing numbers in these divisions.

    $\frac{1}{9} \div \text{.............} = \frac{1}{36}$ $\frac{3}{7} \div \text{.............} = \frac{1}{7}$

    _____
    1 mark

2. Follow the rules of **BODMAS** to work out these calculations.

    $60 \div 5 + 5 = \text{..................}$ $9 - 6 \div 3 = \text{..................}$

    $50 \times 2 \div 10 = \text{..................}$ $7 + 6 \times 5 = \text{..................}$

    _____
    2 marks

3. An online petition has got **3 652 400** signatures.
    What is the value of the **6** in this number?

    ....

    _____
    1 mark

4. Fill in the missing values in these conversions.

    7.109 litres = ... ml   5 ml = ... litres

    _____
    1 mark

5. A holiday company split **3781 customers** equally between
    11 hotels and put the remaining customers into villas.
    How many customers do they put in villas?

    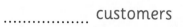

    .... customers

    _____
    1 mark

6. Draw an isosceles triangle that has **two 7 cm sides** and a **35° angle** between them.

7. A van has a weight limit of **3000 kg**.
   It is currently at **99%** of its weight limit.
   How many kg is it carrying?

.... kg

8. In the patterns below, each shape has a value.
   The total value of each pattern is shown.

Work of the value of each shape.

Value: 15

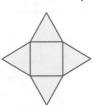

Value: 24

△ = ...

□ = ...

Score: [   ]

Warm up

1. Round these numbers to the **nearest 1000**.

   9 784 100 ....   6 799 600 ....

   _____
1 mark

2. Complete these multiplications.

   0.9 × 9 = ...   1.2 × 8 = ...

   2.44 × 2 = ...   3.21 × 4 = ...

   _____
2 marks

3. What **percentages** of these grids are shaded?

   .... %   .... %

   _____
2 marks

4. Luis has scored **4**, **5**, **7** and **8** in his last four magic exams. What is his **mean** exam score?

   ....   _____
1 mark

5. An equilateral triangle was enlarged by a **scale factor of 5**.
   After the enlargement, each side was **150 cm** long.
   What was the **perimeter before** the enlargement?

   .... cm

6. Join up fractions and divisions that are **equivalent**.

$$\frac{10}{16} \qquad 1\frac{6}{10} \qquad \frac{14}{16}$$

$$14 \div 16 \qquad 5 \div 8 \qquad 16 \div 10$$

7. The formula for the term in **position n** of a sequence
   is **8n + 3**. What is the **100th term** in the sequence?

   ....

8. A builder is carrying a 5 kg case of sand with a hole in.
   Each second, 18 g of sand pours out of the case.
   How many kg of sand are left in the case after
   she's been carrying it for 2 minutes?

   .... kg

   Score:

Warm up

1. Circle the numbers that have a **3** in the **thousandths** place.

    3.753   3215.351   32.003   1.734   3860.335

    _____
    1 mark

2. Work out these percentage calculations.

    10% of 200 = ...   5% of 500 = ...

    30% of 70 = ...   70% of 120 = ...

    _____
    2 marks

3. Teresa's fitness watch records how far she walks each day. On Monday she walked **4.524 km** and on Tuesday she walked **2450 m**. How many **km** did she walk in total?

    .... km   _____
    1 mark

4. Find the size of the **smallest** share when:

    480 is split in the ratio 1 : 3

    ....   _____
    1 mark

    600 is split in the ratio 3 : 7

    ....   _____
    1 mark

5. The graph on the right can be used to convert between two units of capacity — **gallons** and **pints**.

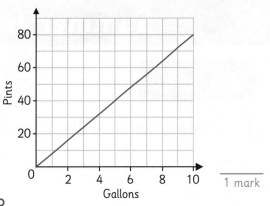

How many pints are in 5 gallons?

.... pints

How many gallons are in 360 pints?

.... gallons

6. The letters in this equation stand for **whole numbers bigger than 0**.

$$(M + 3) \times N = 18$$

List **all** the possible pairs of values of M and N.

M = ...   N = ...

M = ...   N = ...

M = ...   N = ...

7. The two cuboids below have the same volume. What is the length of side x?

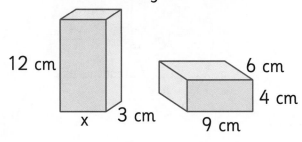

12 cm

3 cm

x

6 cm

4 cm

9 cm

.... cm

Score:

Warm up

1. Write down the **rule** for each of these sequences.

   −7   −1   5   11   ....
   1 mark

   47   32   17   2   ....
   1 mark

2. Circle the **two prime numbers**.

   21   33   37   54   63   77   89
   1 mark

3. Write the number **8 740 322** in **words**.

   ....

   ....
   1 mark

4. **36 pupils** were asked to choose their favourite dinosaur. The results are shown in this pie chart.

   What **angle** on the pie chart represents **one pupil**?

   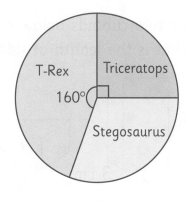

   .... °
   1 mark

   How many pupils chose **Stegosaurus**?

   .... pupils
   1 mark

5. A cafe serves **3 cups of tea** for every **5 cups of coffee**.
    One day they served **72 drinks** in total.
    How many cups of coffee did they serve?

.... cups of coffee

6. These three shapes have the **same perimeter**.

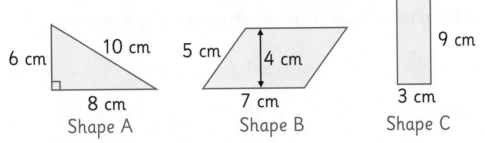

6 cm 10 cm	5 cm 4 cm	9 cm
8 cm	7 cm	3 cm
Shape A	Shape B	Shape C

Put these shapes in order. Start with the **smallest area**.

Shape ....   Shape ....   Shape ....

7. Crocs on ice have sold 7732 tickets for their Saturday and
    Sunday shows. 3017 people went to the Saturday show.
    42 people can fit on a row of seats. How many
    rows of seats will be needed for the Sunday show?

.... rows

Score:

Warm up

1. Work out this calculation **in your head**.

    5 720 000 + (37 000 − 21 000) = ...

    1 mark

2. Fill in the gaps in these number sentences using **<, =** or **>**.

    0.53 .... $\frac{3}{5}$ 0.82 .... 82%

    $\frac{1}{20}$ .... 0.04 $\frac{31}{50}$ 64%

    2 marks

3. The lowest outside temperature ever recorded on Earth is
    −89 °C and the highest outside temperature is **56 °C**.
    What is the **difference** between these temperatures?

    .... °C

    1 mark

4. If you take a number **p**, divide it by **5** and add **7** you get **10**.

    Circle the equation which shows this.

    (p + 7) ÷ 5 = 10   (p − 7) × 5 = 10 $\frac{p}{5}$ + 7 = 10

    1 mark

    What is the value of **p**?

    p = ...

    1 mark

5. Look at the shape on the grid below.

   Reflect shape P
   in the **y-axis**.
   Label this shape Q.

   Reflect shape P
   in the **x-axis**.
   Label this shape R.

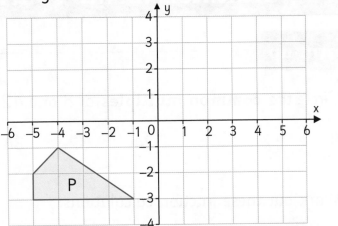

6. Iona, Liam and Lily have all grown a watermelon.

   Iona's watermelon has a mass of $1\frac{5}{18}$ **kg**,

   Liam's is $\frac{5}{4}$ **kg** and Lily's is $1\frac{2}{9}$ **kg**.

   Who has the **heaviest** watermelon? Show your working.

   ....

7. A football kit is made up of a shirt and a pair of shorts.
   Six shirts cost £120 and four pairs of shorts cost £60.

   How many full kits can you buy with £525?

   .... kits

   Score:

Summer Term: Workout 10

Warm up

1. Circle the **common multiples** of 8 and 12.

    8   12   16   24   32   36   40   48   _____

    1 mark

2. Work out these fraction calculations.

    $\frac{1}{4} \div 8 =$ .... $\frac{1}{2} \div 5 =$ ....

    $\frac{7}{8} \div 3 =$ .... $\frac{3}{11} \div 6 =$ ....

    2 marks

3. A recipe uses **2 eggs** for every **150 g of flour**.

    How much flour is needed if 4 eggs are used?

    .... g

    1 mark

    How many eggs are needed if 600 g of flour is used?

    .... eggs

    1 mark

4. What is the **radius** of a circle with a **diameter of 41 cm**?

    .... cm

    1 mark

---

5. What is the **sum of the interior angles** of this regular polygon?

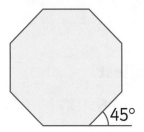

45°

.... °

2 marks

6. Circle the formula that gives the **largest value of b** when **d = 10**.

b = 5 + d   b = 2d − 6   b = d ÷ 5 + 11

1 mark

7. Hariette has drawn a parallelogram with **two 6 cm sides** and **two 5 cm sides**. She says, "the area of my parallelogram is 30 cm²." Do you agree with Hariette? Explain your answer.

....

....

1 mark

8. Each day, Farmer Pod uses 2.785 litres of fuel in his tractor. His tractor had 30 litres of fuel at the start of Monday. How much fuel would it have left at the end of Friday?

.... litres

2 marks

Score:

1. Put these numbers in order. Start with the **smallest**.

    7 485 200   7 484 900   7 485 100

    ....

        smallest   largest | 1 mark

2. Complete these fraction calculations.

    $$\frac{2}{9} + \frac{1}{4} = \frac{8}{36} + \text{............} = \text{............}$$
    | 1 mark

    $$\frac{7}{10} - \frac{1}{3} = \text{............} - \frac{10}{30} = \text{............}$$
    | 1 mark

3. Work out the **area** of the **shaded part** of this rectangle.

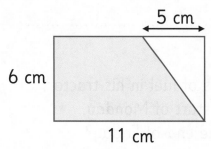

    .... cm² | 2 marks

4. A **62.3 mm** sausage is chopped into **5 equal pieces**.
    How long is each piece? Give your answer as a **decimal**.

    .... mm | 1 mark

---

5. Use this formula to answer the questions: $y = \dfrac{x-5}{2}$

What is the value of y when x = 19?

y = ...

1 mark

What is the value of x when y = 10?

x = ...

1 mark

6. Convert the following distances.

20 miles to km

.... km

1 mark

88 km to miles

.... miles

1 mark

7. A spaceship is 236 500 miles from Planet Pollo.
It gets 2500 miles closer every hour.
How far will it be from Planet Pollo in exactly one day?
Give your answer to the nearest 5000 miles.

.... miles

2 marks

Score: [   ]

Warm up

1. Work out this calculation **in your head**.

   9 400 000 – (470 000 – 360 000) = ...

   1 mark

2. Write these amounts as **decimals**.

   $\frac{19}{20}$ ....

   $\frac{24}{200}$ ....

   $1\frac{12}{25}$ ....

   $3\frac{19}{50}$ ....

   2 marks

3. **Translate** the shape drawn on the grid **+4 units horizontally** and **–3 units vertically**.

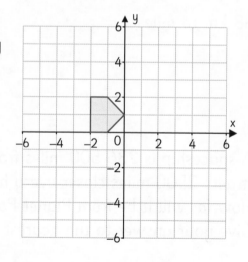

   1 mark

4. Describe the translation when point (5, 3) moves to (–3, –6).

   The point has been translated

   .... units horizontally and

   .... units vertically.

   1 mark

5. In an animal shelter, there are **2 dogs** for every **7 cats**.
   There are a **total of 108** dogs and cats.
   How many more cats are there than dogs?

   ....

   2 marks

6. The diagram below shows a **kite**. Find the size of **angle m**.

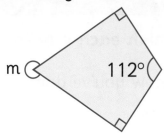

112°

m = ... °

_____
1 mark

7. To work out the number of sandwiches needed for a party you **double** the number of guests and **add 10**.

Write a word formula for working out the number of sandwiches from the number of guests.

....

_____
1 mark

Use your formula to work out how many sandwiches are needed for **70 guests**.

.... sandwiches

_____
1 mark

8. Justine has grown six carrots. They have a mean length of 25 cm. Three of the carrots are 20 cm long, and two of the carrots are 28 cm long.

How long is the sixth carrot?

.... cm

_____
2 marks

Score: [   ]

Progress Chart

Fill in the progress chart after you finish each workout.

Put your scores in here to see how you've done.
Each workout is out of 12 marks.

	Autumn Term	Spring Term	Summer Term
Workout 1			
Workout 2			
Workout 3			
Workout 4			
Workout 5			
Workout 6			
Workout 7			
Workout 8			
Workout 9			
Workout 10			
Workout 11			
Workout 12			

Answers

Autumn Term

Workout 1 — pages 2-3

1. $16.5 \times 100 = \mathbf{1650}$ $87 \div 100 = \mathbf{0.87}$
   $1.24 \times 1000 = \mathbf{1240}$ $5720 \div 1000 = \mathbf{5.72}$
   2 marks for all 4 correct,
   otherwise 1 mark for any 2 correct

2. $2 - 9 = \mathbf{-7}$ $-3 + 5 = \mathbf{2}$
   $3 - 7 = \mathbf{-4}$ $-2 + 8 = \mathbf{6}$
   2 marks for all 4 correct,
   otherwise 1 mark for any 2 correct

3. Angle $p = 180° - 60° - 45° = \mathbf{75°}$ 1 mark

4. 25 cm $\approx 25 \div 5 \times 2 = \mathbf{10\ inches}$ 1 mark

5. **973 221** 1 mark   **122 379** 1 mark

6. $\quad\ 0\ 5\ 4\ 2\ r\ 1$
   $6\ \overline{)\ 3\ ^3 2\ ^2 5\ ^1 3}$ so he needs **543 boxes** 1 mark

7. Each interval is $1 \div 5 = 0.2\ °C$
   Igloo A $= 1.6 - 0.2 = 1.4\ °C$ increase 1 mark
   Igloo B $= 1.2 - 0 = 1.2\ °C$ increase 1 mark
   The temperature in Igloo A increased by
   $1.4 - 1.2 = \mathbf{0.2\ °C}$ more. 1 mark

Workout 2 — pages 4-5

1. $5\underline{1}7\ 802$ — **500 000** $472\ 0\underline{0}0$ — **2000**
   $7\underline{6}4\ 245$ — **60 000** $871\ 2\underline{9}9$ — **90**
   2 marks for all 4 correct,
   otherwise 1 mark for any 2 correct

2. $500 \times 5 = \mathbf{2500}$ $7000 \times 8 = \mathbf{56\,000}$
   $2800 \div 4 = \mathbf{700}$ $5400 \div 9 = \mathbf{600}$
   2 marks for all 4 correct,
   otherwise 1 mark for any 2 correct

3.
   1 mark for shape B drawn correctly,
   1 mark for shape C drawn correctly

4. $\frac{3}{7} + \frac{6}{7} = \frac{9}{7} = 1\frac{2}{7}$ 1 mark

5. Length $= 132 \div 11 = 12$ cm 1 mark
   Perimeter $= 11 + 12 + 11 + 12 = \mathbf{46\ cm}$ 1 mark

6. 7 mins 50 secs + 2 mins = 9 mins 50 secs
   9 mins 50 secs + 30 secs
   $= \mathbf{10\ mins\ 20\ secs}$ 1 mark

7. CCCXIV = 314 1 mark
   $1809 - 314 = \mathbf{1495\ years}$ 1 mark

Workout 3 — pages 6-7

1. 2.5 — **3** 4.9 — **5**
   7.15 — **7** 8.22 — **8**
   2 marks for all 4 correct,
   otherwise 1 mark for any 2 correct

2. $6400 + \mathbf{3000} = 9400$
   $\mathbf{89\,100} - 2000 = 87\,100$
   $5470 - \mathbf{1100} = 4370$
   $\mathbf{15\,270} + 4400 = 19\,670$
   2 marks for all 4 correct,
   otherwise 1 mark for any 2 correct

3. $100\% - 17\% - 26\% - 30\% = \mathbf{27\%}$ 1 mark

4. $\quad\quad\ 4\ 5\ 2$
   $\quad\ \times\ \ 2\ 3$
   $\overline{\quad 1\ 3\,_1 5\ 6}$
   $\quad\ 9\,_1 0\ 4\ 0$
   $\overline{\ \mathbf{1\ 0\ 3\ 9\ 6}}$ 1 mark

5. $A = \frac{2}{3} = \frac{8}{12}$ full and $C = \frac{5}{6} = \frac{10}{12}$ full 1 mark
   So the correct order is:
   Beaker C, Beaker A, Beaker B 1 mark

6. $62°$ is an acute angle — **true**
   Angles around a point add up to $180°$ — **false**
   Obtuse angles are smaller than acute angles.
   — **false**
   A right angle is exactly $90°$ — **true**
   2 marks for all 4 correct,
   otherwise 1 mark for any 2 correct

7. 1.26 m = 126 cm = 1260 mm 1 mark
   $\quad\quad\ 0\ 1\ 4\ 0$
   $9\ \overline{)\ 1\ ^1 2\ ^3 6\ 0}$ so he used **140 bricks** 1 mark

Workout 4 — pages 8-9

1. $12.9, 13.3, \mathbf{13.7}, \mathbf{14.1}, \mathbf{14.5}$ 1 mark

2. $1200 + 7000 = \mathbf{8200}$
   $58\,300 - 5000 = \mathbf{53\,300}$
   $7420 - 1400 = \mathbf{6020}$
   $16\,500 + 9300 = \mathbf{25\,800}$
   2 marks for all 4 correct,
   otherwise 1 mark for any 2 correct

3. **Two million, three hundred and thirty two thousand, eight hundred and fifty** 1 mark

4. **100** 1 mark   **1000** 1 mark

5. **48 cm³** 1 mark

6. 9.8<u>3</u>1 — **0.8 or 8 tenths**
   15.78<u>2</u> — **0.002 or 2 thousandths** 1 mark

7. 0.352 × 1000 = **352 seconds** 1 mark

8. $\frac{1}{5}$ × 2000 = 400 have one eye 1 mark

   $\frac{3}{4}$ × 2000 = 1500 have two eyes 1 mark

   2000 − 1500 − 400 = 100 have three eyes.
   Total = 400 + (1500 × 2) + (100 × 3)
   = **3700 eyes** 1 mark

Workout 5 — pages 10-11

1. **1, 2, 5, 10, 25** and **50** 1 mark

2. 0.34 = **34%** $\frac{29}{100}$ = **29%**

   0.8 = **80%** $\frac{2}{5}$ = **40%**

   2 marks for all 4 correct,
   otherwise 1 mark for any 2 correct

3. Difference between −15 and −7 = **8 °C** 1 mark
   Difference between 31 and −15 = **46 °C** 1 mark

4. **2 000 000** and **9 000 000** 1 mark

5.
   1 mark

6. 42 000 + 20 000 + 96 500 = 158 500 1 mark
   = **£160 000** to the nearest £10 000 1 mark

7. 233 × 5 = 1165 and 387 × 3 = 1161 1 mark
   1165 + 1161 = 2326 sweets in total 1 mark
   ```
       0 2 9 0 r 6
   8 ⟌ 2 ²2 ³7 2  6
   ```
   so **6 sweets** are left. 1 mark

Workout 6 — pages 12-13

1. 12 087 > 12 078   475 400 > 457 400
   152 100 < 152 500   945 500 < 954 200
   2 marks for all 4 correct,
   otherwise 1 mark for any 2 correct

2. $\frac{1}{8}$ × 5 = $\frac{5}{8}$ $\frac{3}{11}$ × 3 = $\frac{9}{11}$ 1 mark

3. 9 ÷ 3 + 6 = 9 ✔ 1 mark
   11 + 2 × 2 = 15 ✔ 1 mark

4.
   130°
   1 mark

5. 320 000 − 50 000 × 4
   = 320 000 − 200 000 = **120 000** 1 mark
   (432 000 + 123 000) − 40 000
   = 555 000 − 40 000 = **515 000** 1 mark

6. 2848 × 52 ≈ **3000 × 50** 1 mark
   3000 × 50 = **150 000 km** 1 mark

7. Badminton lasts for 2 hours 50 minutes
   Hopathon lasts for 1 hour 15 minutes
   So Badminton lasts for 1 hour and 35 minutes
   longer, which is 60 + 35 = **95 minutes**.
   1 mark for working out how long one event
   lasts, 1 mark for the correct answer

Workout 7 — pages 14-15

1. **3.54, 3.5, 3.45, 3.402, 3.4**
   2 marks for the correct order, otherwise
   1 mark for any 3 in the correct position

2. $\frac{4}{6}$, $\frac{10}{15}$, $\frac{20}{30}$ and $\frac{30}{45}$
   2 marks for all 4 correct,
   otherwise 1 mark for any 2 correct

3. ```
           0 3 5 6 r 3
     12 ⟌ 4 ⁴2 ⁶7 ⁷5
   ```
   so **357 pots** 1 mark

4. **57%** 1 mark   **88%** 1 mark

5. **cone** and **cylinder** 1 mark

6. ```
         2 6 4 7
     ×     5 4
     1 0₂5₁8₂8
     1 3₃2₂3₃5 0
     1 4 2 9₁3 8
   ```
   so **142 938 pages** 1 mark
   ```
         0 1 2 0 r 7
     22 ⟌ 2 6 4 7
     − 2 2
         4 4
       − 4 4
         0 7
   ```
   so **7 magazines** left 1 mark

7. 2.7 cm = 27 mm and 1.2 cm = 12 mm
   The missing sides are:
   21 − 12 = 9 mm and 27 − 9 = 18 mm 1 mark
   So the perimeter is:
   27 + 21 + 9 + 9 + 18 + 12 = **96 mm** 1 mark

Workout 8 — pages 16-17

1. **57 049**   **600 202** 1 mark

2. **8.44** and **8.35** 1 mark

3. **70**, **140** and **350** 1 mark

4. **26 m²** 1 mark   **25 m²** 1 mark

5. Factors of 18: 1, 2, 3, 6, 9, 18
   Factors of 42: 1, 2, 3, 6, 7, 14, 21, 42
   Common factors: **1, 2, 3, 6** 1 mark

6. $\frac{19}{50} = \frac{38}{100}$ = 38% are spotty 1 mark
   100% − 45% − 38% = **17%** are plain 1 mark

7. **None.** 1 mark Any common multiple will have
   3 and 11 as factors so won't be prime. 1 mark

8. 07:55 to 10:10 is 2 hours 15 mins 1 mark
   In 2 hours it turns 2 × 360° = 720°
   In 15 minutes it turns 360° ÷ 4 = 90°
   So in total it turns 720° + 90° = **810°** 1 mark

Workout 9 — pages 18-19

1. 87.10 — **80**   5.68 — **0.08**
   0.85 — **0.8**   18.77 — **8**
   2 marks for all 4 correct,
   otherwise 1 mark for any 2 correct

2. 122 400, **112 400, 102 400, 92 400** 1 mark

3. $\frac{20}{25} = \frac{4}{5}$ $\frac{28}{70} = \frac{4}{10} = \frac{2}{5}$ 1 mark

4. **240°** 1 mark

5. $\frac{23}{10} = \frac{69}{30}, \frac{11}{5} = \frac{66}{30}, \frac{34}{15} = \frac{68}{30}$
   So $\frac{23}{10}$ is the largest. 1 mark

6. 160 × 20 = 3200 g 1 mark
   3200 g ÷ 1000 = **3.2 kg** 1 mark

7. $\frac{2}{3} = \frac{4}{6}$ so $\frac{2}{3}$ is smaller 1 mark
   $\frac{5}{6} = \frac{10}{12}$ so $\frac{11}{12}$ is bigger
   $\frac{7}{8} = \frac{21}{24}$ and $\frac{5}{6} = \frac{20}{24}$ so $\frac{7}{8}$ is bigger
   $\frac{7}{9} = \frac{14}{18}$ and $\frac{5}{6} = \frac{15}{18}$ so $\frac{7}{9}$ is smaller 1 mark

8. Full price is £23 340 × 2 = £46 680 1 mark
   Look at the table for two amounts which add to
   give £46 680. £14 530 + £32 150 = £46 680
   He bought a **Sapphire** and a **Diamond** 1 mark

Workout 10 — pages 20-21

1. **153 333, 153 533, 155 233, 155 323** 1 mark

2. 2   5   ~~7~~   ~~9~~   11   ~~15~~   19
   23   ~~25~~   ~~26~~   31   ~~33~~   37
   2 marks for all 6 crossed out, otherwise
   1 mark for any 3 correctly crossed out

3. $7^2 + 2^3 = 49 + 8 = $ **57** 1 mark

4. 1.41 × 2 = **2.82 miles** 1 mark
   1.41 × 7 = **9.87 miles** 1 mark

5.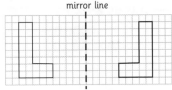
   1 mark

6. $1\frac{1}{3} = 1\frac{8}{24}$ and $\frac{5}{8} = \frac{15}{24}$ 1 mark
   In total he has $1\frac{8}{24} + \frac{15}{24} = 1\frac{23}{24}$ **kg** 1 mark
   $1\frac{8}{24} = \frac{32}{24}$ so the sweet potatoes weigh
   $\frac{32}{24} - \frac{15}{24} = \frac{17}{24}$ **kg** more 1 mark

7. Each week she drinks (110 × 5) + (150 × 2)
   = 550 + 300 = 850 ml 1 mark
   So in 6 weeks she drinks 6 × 850 = 5100 ml
   5100 ÷ 1000 = **5.1 litres** 1 mark

Workout 11 — pages 22-23

1. 0.93 × **100** = 93   45.1 ÷ **10** = 4.51
   7.84 × **1000** = 7840   547 ÷ **100** = 5.47
   2 marks for all 4 correct,
   otherwise 1 mark for any 2 correct

2. **4, 36** and **64** 1 mark

3. E.g.
   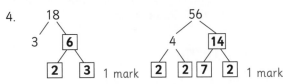
   1 mark

4.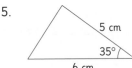
   1 mark   1 mark

5.
   5 cm
   35°
   6 cm
   2 marks for a fully correct triangle, otherwise
   1 mark for drawing the sides or angle correctly

   34 mm 1 mark (allow 33 mm or 35 mm)

6. 87 542 rounded to the nearest **100** is 87 500.
   587 542 rounded to the nearest **10 000** is
   590 000. 1 mark for both correct

7. $\frac{2}{3} = \frac{4}{6}$, so after making the bread,
   Jenny has $2\frac{5}{6} - \frac{4}{6} = 2\frac{1}{6}$ kg 1 mark
   Grandma has $2\frac{1}{6} \times 3 = 6\frac{3}{6} = 6\frac{1}{2}$ **kg** 1 mark

Answers

Workout 12 — pages 24-25

1. 9 — **IX**   23 — **XXIII**
   54 — **LIV**   112 — **CXII**
   2 marks for all 4 correct,
   otherwise 1 mark for any 2 correct

2. $1\frac{1}{4} = \frac{5}{4}$ $4\frac{1}{2} = \frac{9}{2}$
   $2\frac{3}{4} = \frac{11}{4}$ $3\frac{2}{3} = \frac{11}{3}$
   2 marks for all 4 correct,
   otherwise 1 mark for any 2 correct

3.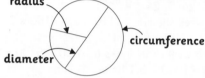
   radius
   circumference
   diameter
   1 mark

4. $10 \times 2 = $ **20 cm** 1 mark

5. **Triangular prism** 1 mark
   Isosceles triangle 1 mark

6. Kim's house is worth
   £428 440 ÷ 2 = £214 220 1 mark
   So Lydia's house is worth
   £214 220 + £25 200 = **£239 420** 1 mark

7. 4.5 litres = 4500 ml and 0.3 litres = 300 ml
   So he pours out 9 × 300 = 2700 ml
   and 4 × 220 = 880 ml 1 mark
   So there is 4500 − 2700 − 880 = 920 ml left
   920 ml = **0.92 litres** 1 mark

Spring Term

Workout 1 — pages 26-27

1. 42 300 — **42 000**   678 510 — **679 000**
   899 654 — **900 000**   4 972 542 — **4 973 000**
   2 marks for all 4 correct,
   otherwise 1 mark for any 2 correct

2. $\frac{2}{3}$ and $\frac{4}{6}$ 1 mark

3. Difference between 43 and −21 = **64 m** 1 mark

4. $\frac{3}{4} \times \frac{2}{5} = \frac{6}{20} = \frac{3}{10}$ 1 mark
   $\frac{5}{6} \times \frac{4}{10} = \frac{20}{60} = \frac{1}{3}$ 1 mark

5. **Circumference** 1 mark

6.
   ```
         8 6 3 2
       ×     1 6
     5 1₃7₁9₁2
     8 6 3 2 0
   1 3 8₁1₁1 2
   ```
   so they make **138 112** 1 mark

7. $\frac{3}{10} \div 2 = \frac{3}{20}$, $\frac{9}{11} \div 3 = \frac{3}{11}$ and $\frac{8}{9} \div 8 = \frac{1}{9}$
   2 marks for all 3 correctly circled,
   otherwise 1 mark for any 2 correctly circled

8. The biggest difference was in 2018 when
   bar 1 was £1.35 and bar 2 was £1.10. 1 mark
   £1.35 − £1.10 = £0.25 = **25p** 1 mark

Workout 2 — pages 28-29

1. **25, 75, 300, 450, 1025**
   2 marks for all 5 correctly circled,
   otherwise 1 mark for any 3 correctly circled

2. 5400 + 1200 = **6600**
   34 400 − 3100 = **31 300**
   9870 − 2220 = **7650**
   43 960 + 5030 = **48 990**
   2 marks for all 4 correct,
   otherwise 1 mark for any 2 correct

3. **Yes because** $\frac{14}{64} = \frac{7}{32} = $ **7 ÷ 32** 1 mark

4.
   ```
      2 8 7 . 1 5
   2 ⌐5¹7¹4 . 3¹0
   ```
   1 mark

5. E.g.

   2 marks for a fully correct net, otherwise
   1 mark if at least 4 faces are drawn correctly

6.
   ```
      0 . 3 7 5
   8 ⌐3 .³0⁶0⁴0
   ```
   1 mark
   ```
       0 . 3 5
   20 ⌐7 .⁷0¹⁰0
   ```
   1 mark

7. 7 teaspoons = 5.12 × 7 = 35.84 ml 1 mark
   So there is 50 − 35.84 = **14.16 ml** left 1 mark

Workout 3 — pages 30-31

1. $3^3 = $ **27** and $7^2 = $ **49** 1 mark

2. $\frac{3}{7} \times 4 = \frac{12}{7}$ $\frac{8}{9} \times 7 = \frac{56}{9}$
   $\frac{4}{5} \times 12 = \frac{48}{5}$ $\frac{5}{6} \times 5 = \frac{25}{6}$
   2 marks for all 4 correct,
   otherwise 1 mark for any 2 correct

3. 100% − 53% = 47% = $\frac{47}{100}$ 1 mark

4.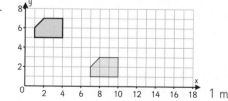
   1 mark

5.

$$8.74 \xrightarrow{\times 100} \textbf{874} \xrightarrow{\div 1000} \textbf{0.874}$$ 1 mark

6. Sid: $\frac{7}{20} = \frac{35}{100} = 35\%$ Meg: $\frac{1}{3} = 33.33...\%$
   and Zainab: 34% so **Sid** has finished more levels.
   1 mark for converting one value between
   a fraction and percentage correctly,
   1 mark for the correct answer

7. 10% of 700 ml = 700 ÷ 10 = 70 ml
   5% of 700 ml = 70 ÷ 2 = 35 ml
   Bottle A: 15% of 700 ml = 70 + 35 = 105 ml
   10% of 300 ml = 300 ÷ 10 = 30 ml
   Bottle B: 40% of 300 ml = 30 × 4 = 120 ml
   So **bottle B** has more liquid.
   1 mark for finding the amount of liquid
   in one bottle, 1 mark for the correct answer

8. 6 875 000 − 2 815 000 = 4 060 000   1 mark
   4 060 000 × 3 = **12 180 000 cups**   1 mark

Workout 4 — pages 32-33

1. **74.83** and **1.847**   1 mark

2. 5000 × 30 = **150 000**   32 000 ÷ 80 = **400**
   900 × 700 = **630 000**   60 000 ÷ 200 = **300**
   2 marks for all 4 correct,
   otherwise 1 mark for any 2 correct

3. **1**, **2** and **4**   1 mark

4. Lev gets $\frac{2}{3}$ of the peanuts.
   270 ÷ 3 × 2 = 90 × 2 = **180 peanuts**   1 mark

5. **£2 145 000**   1 mark

6.

	No obtuse angles	Obtuse angles
2 lines of symmetry	**Rectangle**	**Rhombus**
More than 2 lines of symmetry	**Equilateral Triangle**	**Regular Pentagon**

   2 marks for all 4 correct,
   otherwise 1 mark for any 2 correct

7. 30 ÷ 5 × 2 = **12 pupils**   1 mark
   30 − 12 = **18 pupils**   1 mark

8. Short side = (11 − 7) ÷ 2 = 2 cm   1 mark
   Area of each rectangle = 2 × 7 = 14 cm²
   Total shaded area = 14 × 4 = **56 cm²**   1 mark

Workout 5 — pages 34-35

1. $\frac{5}{8} > \frac{1}{2}$ $\frac{1}{3} < \frac{4}{9}$ $\frac{3}{4} = \frac{9}{12}$ $\frac{3}{5} < \frac{7}{10}$
   2 marks for all 4 correct,
   otherwise 1 mark for any 2 correct

2. 747 300, **748 300**, **749 300**, **750 300**   1 mark

3. 7 × 5 = **35 cm**   1 mark

4. Check numbers ending in 1, 3, 7 or 9.
   51 ÷ 3 = 17 so 51 is not prime.
   53 only divides by 1 and 53 so is prime.   1 mark
   57 ÷ 3 = 19 so 57 is not prime.
   59 only divides by 1 and 59 so is prime.   1 mark

5. 9 humans = 3 × 3
   So there are 8 × 3 = **24 robots**   1 mark

   72 robots = 8 × 9
   So there are 3 × 9 = **27 humans**   1 mark

6. 5.6 m = 5.6 × 100 = 560 cm   1 mark
   Scale factor = 560 ÷ 80 = **7**   1 mark

7.
   $$18 \overline{\smash{)}5\,{}^54\,3\,{}^34}$$ 3 0 1 r 16   1 mark
   Each section has the same number of seats
   so there shouldn't be a remainder.
   So **he has not counted correctly**.   1 mark

Workout 6 — pages 36-37

1. 0.15 — **0.2**   7.04 — **7.0**
   16.91 — **16.9**   42.97 — **43.0**
   2 marks for all 4 correct,
   otherwise 1 mark for any 2 correct

2. $3\frac{6}{7} - \frac{4}{7} = 3\frac{2}{7}$ $2\frac{1}{5} - \frac{2}{5} = 1\frac{4}{5}$ 1 mark

3. Rule: **Add 7**   Next term: **23**   1 mark
   Rule: **Subtract 150**   Next term: **100**   1 mark

4.    1 mark

5. (40 × 2.5) + 10 = **110 minutes**   1 mark

6. Ferry A: 11:30 till 13:17 = 1 hour 47 mins
   Ferry B: 12:55 till 14:39 = 1 hour 44 mins
   Ferry C: 14:20 till 16:05 = 1 hour 45 mins
   So **Ferry B** will take the least time.
   1 mark for working out how long it takes
   2 ferries correctly, 1 mark for the correct answer

7. When n = 1: 4 × 1 + 1 = **5**
   When n = 2: 4 × 2 + 1 = **9**
   When n = 3: 4 × 3 + 1 = **13**   1 mark

8. Tamal rounds it to 1 900 000.
   Una rounds it to 1 860 000. So the difference is
   1 900 000 − 1 860 000 = **40 000**
   1 mark for working out what either person
   rounded it to, 1 mark for the correct answer

Workout 7 — pages 38-39

1. $\frac{4}{5}$, $1\frac{1}{5}$, $1\frac{3}{5}$, **2**, $2\frac{2}{5}$ 1 mark

2. $-2 - 6 = -8$ $-4 + 7 = 3$
   $4 - 5 = -1$ $-4 + 6 = 2$
   2 marks for all 4 correct,
   otherwise 1 mark for any 2 correct

3. 25 cm ÷ 2 = **12.5 cm** 1 mark

4. **4x − 7 = 17** 1 mark
   4x = 24 so **x = 6** 1 mark

5. **A = 4, B = 2** 1 mark

6. **8 775 423** 1 mark

7. ☆ **= 1 and** ◯ **= 14** (5 × 1 + 14 = 19)
   ☆ **= 2 and** ◯ **= 9** (5 × 2 + 9 = 19)
   ☆ **= 3 and** ◯ **= 4** (5 × 3 + 4 = 19)
   2 marks for all 3 correct pairs,
   otherwise 1 mark for any 2 correct pairs

8. The number of visitors that were adults:
   $\frac{4}{5}$ × 6000 = 6000 ÷ 5 × 4 = 4800 1 mark
   The number of adults in the butterfly house:
   $\frac{1}{4}$ × 4800 = 4800 ÷ 4 = **1200 adults** 1 mark

Workout 8 — pages 40-41

1. $0.3 = \frac{3}{10}$ $0.29 = \frac{29}{100}$
   $0.62 = \frac{62}{100} = \frac{31}{50}$ $0.15 = \frac{15}{100} = \frac{3}{20}$
   2 marks for all 4 correct,
   otherwise 1 mark for any 2 correct

2. CLXV = **165**   XLVI = **46** 1 mark

3. Gemma's are 1.789 cm = 17.89 mm 1 mark
   So Jessie's are 20.24 − 17.89
   = **2.35 mm** longer 1 mark

4.   3 7 8
     ×   9
     3 4$_7$0$_7$2 so 3.78 × 9 = **34.02** 1 mark

5. E.g.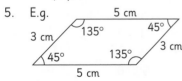
   2 marks for a correct shape, otherwise 1 mark
   for drawing two sides or two angles correctly

6. 8 km ≈ 5 miles and 64 km = 8 km × 8
   64 km ≈ 5 × 8 = 40 miles 1 mark
   So Pete is 45 − 40 = **5 miles** closer 1 mark

Workout 9 — pages 42-43

7. 400 m × 9 = 3600 m   800 m × 12 = 9600 m
   1500 m × 6 = 9000 m 1 mark for all three
   3600 + 9600 + 9000 = 22 200 m
   22 200 m = 22 200 ÷ 1000 = **22.2 km** 1 mark

Workout 9 — pages 42-43

1. 20 × **2000** = 40 000   9000 ÷ **30** = 300
   120 × 300 = 36 000   **32 000** ÷ 200 = 160
   2 marks for all 4 correct,
   otherwise 1 mark for any 2 correct

2. 0.34 = **34%**   0.9 = **90%** 1 mark

3. 0.423 litres = 423 ml and 0.24 litres = 240 ml
   1 mark
   Total = 423 + 199 + 240 = **862 ml** 1 mark

4. 1 mark

5. His mum takes 3 minutes 21 seconds
   3 × 60 + 21 = **201 seconds** 1 mark

6. $\frac{5}{3}$ and $\frac{15}{9}$ 1 mark

7. 6 kg = 6000 g and 3.875 kg = 3875 g 1 mark
   6000 − 3875 − 900 = **1225 g** 1 mark

8.   4 5 1
      ×   8
      3 6$_4$0 8 so it mines 3608 rocks 1 mark
            2 0 0 r 8
      18 ⟌ 3 6 0 8   so **8 rocks** left over 1 mark

Workout 10 — pages 44-45

1. **6900** + 2100 = 9000
   34 400 − **6000** = 28 400
   8560 − 5040 = 3520
   71 080 + **9200** = 80 280
   2 marks for all 4 correct,
   otherwise 1 mark for any 2 correct

2. $0.347 = \frac{3}{10} + \frac{4}{100} + \frac{7}{1000}$
   $0.039 = \frac{3}{100} + \frac{9}{1000}$ 1 mark

3. **6 402 510** 1 mark

4. a = 180° − 40° − 55° = **85°** 1 mark
   b = 360° − 95° − 80° − 75° = **110°** 1 mark

5. 65 − 5 **×** 5 = 40 1 mark

6. The missing angles in the triangle are the same
   and add up to 180° − 38° = 142°.
   So they are 142° ÷ 2 = 71°. x is vertically
   opposite one of these angles, so x = **71°** 1 mark
   y = 180° − 71° = **109°** 1 mark

7. The polygon has $360 \div 60 = 6$ exterior angles.
   So it has 6 sides, which is a **hexagon**. 1 mark

8. 2-digit numbers that are 1 more than a square:
   10, 17, 26, 37, 50, 65, 82 1 mark
   Only 50 has 6 factors — 1, 2, 5, 10, 25 and 50,
   so she is thinking of **50** 1 mark

Workout 11 — pages 46-47

1. 17, 10, **3**, **−4**, **−11** 1 mark

2. $\frac{7}{10} = \mathbf{0.7}$ $\frac{97}{100} = \mathbf{0.97}$

   $\frac{3}{5} = \frac{6}{10} = \mathbf{0.6}$ $\frac{21}{50} = \frac{42}{100} = \mathbf{0.42}$

   2 marks for all 4 correct,
   otherwise 1 mark for any 2 correct

3. $\frac{1}{2} \times 6 \times 10 = \mathbf{30\ cm^2}$ 1 mark
   $8 \times 7 = \mathbf{56\ m^2}$ 1 mark

4. $91 \div 7 = 13$ so **no**, 91 is not prime. 1 mark

5. $5.43 \times 1000 = 5430$ kg
   $5430 + 15 = \mathbf{5445\ kg}$ 1 mark

6. The length and width must add to give 20 cm.

Rectangle	Length	Width	Area
A	2 cm	**18 cm**	**36 cm²**
B	**10 cm**	10 cm	**100 cm²**
C	**1 cm**	**19 cm**	19 cm²

   1 mark for each correct row

7. $1\frac{1}{8} + \frac{2}{3} = 1\frac{3}{24} + \frac{16}{24} = 1\frac{19}{24}$ m 1 mark

   So they have $4 - 1\frac{19}{24} = \mathbf{2\frac{5}{24}}$ **m** left 1 mark

Workout 12 — pages 48-49

1. $5.05 - 2.02 = \mathbf{3.03}$ $5.47 + 1.32 = \mathbf{6.79}$
   $4.3 + 1.59 = \mathbf{5.89}$ $8.5 - 3.48 = \mathbf{5.02}$
   2 marks for all 4 correct,
   otherwise 1 mark for any 2 correct

2. $\frac{7}{10} + \frac{1}{100} + \frac{8}{1000} = \mathbf{0.718}$

   $\frac{3}{10} + \frac{47}{1000} = \mathbf{0.347}$ 1 mark

3. $5 \times 5 \times 5 = \mathbf{125\ cm^3}$ 1 mark

4. $\frac{5}{4} = \frac{30}{24}, \frac{11}{8} = \frac{33}{24}, \frac{4}{3} = \frac{32}{24}, \frac{17}{12} = \frac{34}{24}$

   So the correct order is $\mathbf{\frac{17}{12}, \frac{11}{8}, \frac{4}{3}, \frac{5}{4}}$

   2 marks for the correct order, otherwise
   1 mark for an attempt to put the fractions
   over the same denominator

5. $3 \times 5 \times 2 = \mathbf{30\ cm^3}$ 1 mark
   $4 \times 3 \times 10 = \mathbf{120\ m^3}$ 1 mark

6. Multiples of 9:
   9, 18, 27, 36, 45, 54, 63, 72, 81, 90, 99
   Multiples of 15: 15, 30, 45, 60, 75, 90
   Common multiples are **45** and **90** 1 mark

7. Rounded: $2400 \times 20 = 48\ 000$ 1 mark
   Actual:
   $$\begin{array}{r} 2\ 4\ 0\ 4 \\ \times \qquad 1\ 9 \\ \hline 2\ 1_3 6\ 3_3 6 \\ 2\ 4\ 0\ 4\ 0 \\ \hline 4\ 5\ 6\ 7\ 6 \end{array}$$ 1 mark
   $48\ 000 - 45\ 676 = \mathbf{2324\ crickets}$ 1 mark

Summer Term

Workout 1 — pages 50-51

1. **3 200 000** and **2 000 000** 1 mark

2. $\frac{1}{9} \times \frac{1}{2} = \frac{1}{18}$ $\frac{1}{5} \times \frac{3}{4} = \frac{3}{20}$

   $\frac{3}{8} \times \frac{3}{5} = \frac{9}{40}$ $\frac{7}{9} \times \frac{7}{10} = \frac{49}{90}$

   2 marks for all 4 correct,
   otherwise 1 mark for any 2 correct

3. **Square-based pyramid** 1 mark

4. $$\begin{array}{r} 0\ 2\ 4\ 3 \\ 21\ \overline{)\ 5\ ^5 1\ ^9 0\ ^6 3} \end{array}$$ so **243 books** 1 mark

5. Width $= 10 \div 2 = 5$ cm
   Height $= 5 \times 6 = 30$ cm 1 mark for both
   Volume $= 10 \times 5 \times 30 = \mathbf{1500\ cm^3}$ 1 mark

6.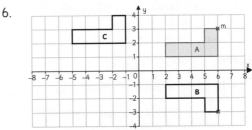

   1 mark for shape B drawn correctly
   1 mark for shape C drawn correctly

   (6, −3) 1 mark

7. Jeans: $\frac{6}{40} = \frac{3}{20} = \frac{15}{100} = 15\%$ off

   Shirt: £25 − £21 = £4 off which is
   $\frac{4}{25} = \frac{16}{100} = 16\%$ off

   The **shirt** has the biggest percentage discount.
   1 mark for finding the percentage discount of
   either item, 1 mark for the correct answer

Answers

Workout 2 — pages 52-53

1. **3 000 000**   **50 000** 1 mark

2. −18 and −30 is **12**   −12 and 20 is **32**
   49 and −10 is **59**   −20 and 37 is **57**
   2 marks for all 4 correct,
   otherwise 1 mark for any 2 correct

3. E.g.

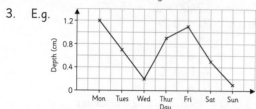

   1 mark for labelling the axes appropriately,
   1 mark for drawing the line graph correctly

   The water depth increases when it rains, so it
   rained on **Wednesday** and **Thursday** 1 mark

4. E.g. **(300 000 + 600 000) × 10** 1 mark

5. 12 + 15 + 9 + 11 + 13 = 60
   60 ÷ 5 = **12** 1 mark

6. 340 × 200 = **68 000 m²** 1 mark

7. E.g. 2 scoops make 300 ÷ 2 = 150 ml 1 mark
   18 scoops make 150 × 9 = 1350 ml 1 mark
   If 1 jar makes 1350 ml then 3 jars make
   1350 × 3 = 4050 ml = **4.05 litres** 1 mark

Workout 3 — pages 54-55

1. **3n + 1** 1 mark

2. 120 000 × **6** = 720 000   3000 × **50** = 150 000
   64 000 ÷ **8** = 8000   810 000 ÷ **90** = 9000
   2 marks for all 4 correct,
   otherwise 1 mark for any 2 correct

3. **Radius** 1 mark

4. $\frac{5}{6} \div 10 = \frac{5}{60} = \frac{1}{12}$ **m** 1 mark

5. $\frac{7}{25} = \frac{28}{100}$ = 28% had water 1 mark
   100% − 32% − 28% = **40%** had both 1 mark

6.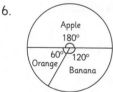

   2 marks for a correct pie chart, otherwise 1 mark
   for one sector drawn and labelled correctly

   1 girl represents 360° ÷ 30 = 12°
   So 4 girls will represent 4 × 12° = **48°** 1 mark

7. The mirror is 41.7 cm = 0.417 m wide.
   Space needed: (0.784 × 2) + 0.417
   = 1.568 + 0.417 = 1.985 m so **yes** they will fit.
   1 mark for the correct calculations,
   1 mark for the correct answer

Workout 4 — pages 56-57

1. 1.578 × 100 = **157.8**   3.87 ÷ 10 = **0.387**
   7.004 × 1000 = **7004**   2508 ÷ 1000 = **2.508**
   2 marks for all 4 correct,
   otherwise 1 mark for any 2 correct

2. $\frac{9}{20} = \frac{45}{100}$ = **0.45** = **45%** 1 mark

3. **(−4, −3)** 1 mark

4. $\frac{1}{4}$ of $\frac{3}{8} = \frac{1}{4} \times \frac{3}{8} = \frac{3}{32}$ 1 mark

5. 2, 3 and 7 are the only prime numbers.
   2 and **7** are also factors of 56 and 84. 1 mark

6. 1 hour 7 minutes = 67 minutes. So he has
   played for 67 + 93 + 29 = 189 minutes 1 mark
   5 hours = 5 × 60 = 300 minutes so he has
   300 − 189 = **111 minutes** left 1 mark

7. $2\frac{7}{12} - 1\frac{3}{4} = 2\frac{7}{12} - 1\frac{9}{12} = \frac{10}{12} = \frac{5}{6}$ 1 mark

8. Length = (20 − 3 − 3) ÷ 2 = 7 cm 1 mark
   After enlarging by scale factor 5, the lengths are
   3 × 5 = 15 cm and 7 × 5 = 35 cm 1 mark
   So the area is 15 × 35 = **525 cm²** 1 mark

Workout 5 — pages 58-59

1. $\frac{1}{9} \div 4 = \frac{1}{36}$ $\frac{3}{7} \div 3 = \frac{1}{7}$ 1 mark

2. 60 ÷ 5 + 5 = **17**   9 − 6 ÷ 3 = **7**
   50 × 2 ÷ 10 = **10**   7 + 6 × 5 = **37**
   2 marks for all 4 correct,
   otherwise 1 mark for any 2 correct

3. **600 000** 1 mark

4. **7109 ml** and **0.005 litres** 1 mark

5.
   ```
     0 3 4 3 r 8
   11 ) 3 ³7 ⁴8 ⁴1
   ```
   So they put **8 customers** in villas. 1 mark

6. E.g.

   2 marks for a correct shape, otherwise 1 mark
   for drawing two sides or the angle correctly

7. 1% of 3000 kg = 3000 ÷ 100 = 30 kg so
   it is carrying 3000 − 30 = **2970 kg** 1 mark

8. The second pattern has 3 more triangles than the first pattern so the value of $3 \times \triangle$ is
   $24 - 15 = 9$. 1 mark
   So $\triangle = 9 \div 3 = \mathbf{3}$ 1 mark
   $\triangle + \square = 15$ so $\square = 15 - 3 = \mathbf{12}$ 1 mark

Workout 6 — pages 60-61

1. 9 784 100 — **9 784 000**
   6 799 600 — **6 800 000** 1 mark

2. $0.9 \times 9 = \mathbf{8.1}$ $1.2 \times 8 = \mathbf{9.6}$
   $2.44 \times 2 = \mathbf{4.88}$ $3.21 \times 4 = \mathbf{12.84}$
   2 marks for all 4 correct,
   otherwise 1 mark for any 2 correct

3. $\dfrac{27}{50} = \dfrac{54}{100} = \mathbf{54\%}$ 1 mark
   $\dfrac{12}{20} = \dfrac{60}{100} = \mathbf{60\%}$ 1 mark

4. Total score = $4 + 5 + 7 + 8 = 24$
   $24 \div 4 = \mathbf{6}$ 1 mark

5. Side length = $150 \div 5 = 30$ cm 1 mark
   Perimeter = $30 \times 3 = \mathbf{90\ cm}$ 1 mark

6.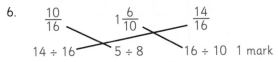
   $\dfrac{10}{16}$ $1\dfrac{6}{10}$ $\dfrac{14}{16}$
   $14 \div 16$ $5 \div 8$ $16 \div 10$ 1 mark

7. $(8 \times 100) + 3 = \mathbf{803}$ 1 mark

8. 2 minutes = $2 \times 60 = 120$ seconds
   So $120 \times 18 = 2160$ g pours out 1 mark
   5 kg = 5000 g so the amount of sand left is
   $5000 - 2160 = 2840$ g = **2.84 kg** 1 mark

Workout 7 — pages 62-63

1. **3.753** and **32.003** 1 mark

2. 10% of 200 = $200 \div 10 = \mathbf{20}$
   5% of 500 = $500 \div 100 \times 5 = \mathbf{25}$
   30% of 70 = $70 \div 10 \times 3 = \mathbf{21}$
   70% of 120 = $120 \div 10 \times 7 = \mathbf{84}$
   2 marks for all 4 correct,
   otherwise 1 mark for any 2 correct

3. 2450 m = 2.45 km
   $4.524 + 2.45 = \mathbf{6.974\ km}$ 1 mark

4. There are $1 + 3 = 4$ shares
   so 1 share is $480 \div 4 = \mathbf{120}$ 1 mark
   There are $3 + 7 = 10$ shares
   so 3 shares are $600 \div 10 \times 3 = \mathbf{180}$ 1 mark

5. 5 gallons = **40 pints** 1 mark
   If 5 gallons = 40 pints then $40 \times 9 = 360$ pints
   is equal to $5 \times 9 = \mathbf{45\ gallons}$ 1 mark

6. **M = 15, N = 1** $(15 + 3) \times 1 = 18$
   M = 6, N = 2 $(6 + 3) \times 2 = 18$
   M = 3, N = 3 $(3 + 3) \times 3 = 18$
   2 marks for all 3 correct pairs,
   otherwise 1 mark for any 2 correct pairs

7. Volume = $9 \times 6 \times 4 = 216$ cm³ 1 mark
   So x = $216 \div 3 \div 12 = 72 \div 12 = \mathbf{6\ cm}$ 1 mark

Workout 8 — pages 64-65

1. **Add 6** 1 mark   **Subtract 15** 1 mark

2. **37** and **89** 1 mark

3. **Eight million, seven hundred and forty thousand, three hundred and twenty two.**
   1 mark

4. One pupil: $360° \div 36 = \mathbf{10°}$ 1 mark
   Stegosaurus = $360° - 90° - 160° = 110°$
   $110 \div 10 = \mathbf{11\ pupils}$ 1 mark

5. 5 out of every 8 cups are coffee.
   $8 \times 9 = 72$ drinks in total so
   $5 \times 9 = \mathbf{45\ cups\ of\ coffee}$ 1 mark

6. Area of Shape A = $\frac{1}{2} \times 8 \times 6 = 24$ cm² 1 mark
   Area of Shape B = $7 \times 4 = 28$ cm² 1 mark
   Area of Shape C = $3 \times 9 = 27$ cm²
   Order: **Shape A, Shape C, Shape B** 1 mark

7. $7732 - 3017 = 4715$ 1 mark
   $$42\ \big|\ \overline{4\ ^4 4\ ^5 7\ ^1 5}\quad \begin{array}{c} 0\ 1\ 1\ 2\ \text{r}\ 11 \end{array}$$
   so **113 rows** 1 mark

Workout 9 — pages 66-67

1. **5 736 000** 1 mark

2. $0.53 < \dfrac{3}{5}$ $0.82 = 82\%$
   $\dfrac{1}{20} > 0.04$ $\dfrac{31}{50} < 64\%$
   2 marks for all 4 correct,
   otherwise 1 mark for any 2 correct

3. $89 + 56 = \mathbf{145\ °C}$ 1 mark

4. $\dfrac{p}{5} + 7 = \mathbf{10}$ 1 mark
   $p = (10 - 7) \times 5 = \mathbf{15}$ 1 mark

5.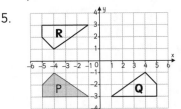
   1 mark for drawing shape Q correctly,
   1 mark for drawing shape R correctly

Answers

6. Iona: $1\frac{5}{18} = 1\frac{10}{36}$ kg

Liam: $\frac{5}{4} = 1\frac{1}{4} = 1\frac{9}{36}$ kg   Lily: $1\frac{2}{9} = 1\frac{8}{36}$ kg

So **Iona** has the heaviest watermelon.

1 mark for putting the fractions over a common denominator, 1 mark for the correct answer

7. Shirt: £120 ÷ 6 = £20   Shorts: £60 ÷ 4 = £15

So one kit costs £20 + £15 = £35   1 mark

$35 \overline{)\,5\,{}^5 2\,{}^{17}5}$ $\quad\overset{0\ \ 1\ \ 5}{}$ so you can buy **15 kits**   1 mark

Workout 10 — pages 68-69

1. **24** and **48**   1 mark

2. $\frac{1}{4} \div 8 = \frac{1}{32}$ $\qquad$ $\frac{1}{2} \div 5 = \frac{1}{10}$

   $\frac{7}{8} \div 3 = \frac{7}{24}$ $\qquad$ $\frac{3}{11} \div 6 = \frac{3}{66} = \frac{1}{22}$

   2 marks for all 4 correct,
   otherwise 1 mark for any 2 correct

3. 4 eggs = 2 eggs × 2
   So 150 × 2 = **300 g** flour is needed   1 mark
   600 g = 150 g × 4
   So 2 × 4 = **8 eggs** are needed   1 mark

4. 41 ÷ 2 = **20.5 cm**   1 mark

5. Each interior angle = 180° − 45° = 135°   1 mark
   Eight interior angles = 135° × 8 = **1080°**   1 mark

6. b = 5 + d gives b = 5 + 10 = 15
   b = 2d − 6 gives b = (2 × 10) − 6 = 14
   b = d ÷ 5 + 11 gives b = 10 ÷ 5 + 11 = 13
   So **b = 5 + d** gives the largest value.   1 mark

7. **No**, the area is the base length multiplied by the height, not the other side length.   1 mark

8. $\begin{array}{r} 2\ 7\ 8\ 5 \\ \times \qquad 5 \\ \hline 1\ 3_3\,9_4\,2_2\,5 \end{array}$ so the farmer uses
   2.785 × 5 = 13.925 litres of fuel   1 mark
   30 − 13.925 = **16.075 litres** left   1 mark

Workout 11 — pages 70-71

1. **7 484 900, 7 485 100, 7 485 200**   1 mark

2. $\frac{2}{9} + \frac{1}{4} = \frac{8}{36} + \frac{9}{36} = \frac{17}{36}$ 1 mark

   $\frac{7}{10} - \frac{1}{3} = \frac{21}{30} - \frac{10}{30} = \frac{11}{30}$ 1 mark

3. Triangle = $\frac{1}{2}$ × 5 × 6 = 15 cm²   1 mark
   Rectangle = 11 × 6 = 66 cm²
   Shaded part = 66 − 15 = **51 cm²**   1 mark

4. $5 \overline{)\,6\,{}^12\,{}^23\,{}^30}$ $\quad\overset{1\ 2\,.\,4\ 6}{}\!\!\!\!\!\!\!\!\!\!\!\!\!{}^{\textstyle .}$ so a piece is **12.46 mm**   1 mark

5. $y = \frac{19 - 5}{2} = \frac{14}{2} = \mathbf{7}$ 1 mark

   $10 = \frac{x - 5}{2}$ so 20 = x − 5 so **x = 25**   1 mark

6. 20 miles ≈ 20 ÷ 5 × 8 = **32 km**   1 mark
   88 km ≈ 88 ÷ 8 × 5 = **55 miles**   1 mark

7. 1 day = 24 hours, so in one day it will be
   2500 × 24 = 60 000 miles closer   1 mark
   236 500 − 60 000 = 176 500 miles left which
   is **175 000 miles** to the nearest 5000.   1 mark

Workout 12 — pages 72-73

1. **9 290 000**   1 mark

2. $\frac{19}{20} = \frac{95}{100} = \mathbf{0.95}$ $\qquad$ $\frac{24}{200} = \frac{12}{100} = \mathbf{0.12}$

   $1\frac{12}{25} = 1\frac{48}{100} = \mathbf{1.48}$ $\qquad$ $3\frac{19}{50} = 3\frac{38}{100} = \mathbf{3.38}$

   2 marks for all 4 correct,
   otherwise 1 mark for any 2 correct

3.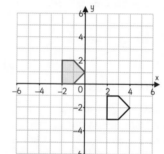

   1 mark

4. The point has been translated **−8** units horizontally and **−9** units vertically.   1 mark

5. 2 out of every 9 animals are dogs
   9 × 12 = 108 animals so
   2 × 12 = 24 dogs and 7 × 12 = 84 cats
   84 − 24 = **60** more cats than dogs
   1 mark for finding the number of dogs or cats,
   1 mark for the correct answer

6. 360° − 90° − 90° − 112° = 68°
   So angle m = 360° − 68° = **292°**   1 mark

7. **Sandwiches = (Guests × 2) + 10**   1 mark

   (70 × 2) + 10 = **150 sandwiches**   1 mark

8. Total length = 25 × 6 = 150 cm   1 mark
   First 5 carrots: (3 × 20) + (2 × 28) = 116 cm so
   the last carrot is 150 − 116 = **34 cm**   1 mark

M6XW21